READING AND NOTE TAKING STUDY GUIDE

WORLD CIVILIZATIONS
THE GLOBAL EXPERIENCE

AP* EDITION

SIXTH EDITION

Peter N. Stearns
George Mason University

Michael Adas
Rutgers University

Stuart B. Schwartz
Yale University

Marc Jason Gilbert
Hawaii Pacific University

D1456097

PEARSON

Boston Columbus Indianapolis New York San Francisco Upper Saddle River
Amsterdam Cape Town Dubai London Madrid Milan Munich Paris Montréal Toronto
Delhi Mexico City São Paulo Sydney Hong Kong Seoul Singapore Taipei Tokyo

Printed in the United States of America

5   16

PEARSON

ISBN 10: 0-13-137179-7
ISBN 13: 978-0-13-137179-8

CONTENTS

CHAPTER 1
From Human Prehistory to the Early Civilizations

Complete the following exercises in order *as you read* the chapter.

INTRODUCTION

Chapter introductions are a valuable guide to the material you are about to read, telling you what topics will be covered and how they fit together. If you keep the "big picture" provided by the introduction in mind as you read the chapter, you will find it much easier to organize your notes, identify important information, and avoid getting lost in the details. With this in mind, re-read the introduction to Chapter 1. As you read, make a list of the key topics you expect to learn about.

Key Topics

_____

_____

_____

_____

_____

_____

_____

_____

_____

_____

_____

_____

_____

_____

_____

_____

_____

_____

_____

_____

1. HUMAN LIFE IN THE ERA OF HUNTERS AND GATHERERS

As you read this section in your textbook, complete the following outline of the section to identify main ideas in each paragraph as well as the key words that inform those ideas.

I. Human species

    A. Emerged 2 to 2.5 million years ago

        1.

        2.

    B.

        1.

        2.

II. Late Paleolithic Developments

    A.

        1.

        2.

    B.

        1.

        2.

    C.

        1.

        2.

    D.

        1.

        2.

2. THE NEOLITHIC REVOLUTION

As you read this section in your textbook, complete the following outline of the section to identify main ideas in each paragraph as well as the key words that inform those ideas.

I. Development of Agriculture
   A. Conditions for agricultural development
      1.
      2.
   B.
      1.
      2.

II. The Geography of Early Agriculture
   A.
      1.
      2.
   B.
      1.
      2.

III. Patterns of Change
   A.
      1.
      2.
   B.
      1.
      2.

IV. Further Technological Change
   A.
      1.
      2.
   B.
      1.
      2.

3. THE NEOLITHIC REVOLUTION

As you read this section in your textbook, complete the following chart to summarize the eras of prehistory before and after the introduction of agriculture.

Eras of Prehistory	
Life Before Farming	**Life After Farming**

Life Before Farming

- _____
  _____
  _____

- _____
  _____
  _____

- _____
  _____
  _____

- _____
  _____
  _____

- _____
  _____
  _____

- _____
  _____
  _____

Life After Farming

- _____
  _____
  _____

- _____
  _____
  _____

- _____
  _____
  _____

- _____
  _____
  _____

- _____
  _____
  _____

- _____
  _____
  _____

4. CIVILIZATION

As you read this section in your textbook, complete the following chart with details from the text to summarize the definition of civilization.

The Development of Civilization

Rise of Cities and Civilizations

- _____
  _____
- _____
  _____
- _____
  _____
- _____
  _____

Features of Civilizations

- _____
- _____
- _____
- _____
- _____
- _____
- _____
- _____
- _____

Changes Over Time

- _____
  _____
- _____
  _____
- _____
  _____

5. CIVILIZATION

As you read this section in your textbook, complete the following chart with details from the text to identify the main ideas about the Sumerian city-states.

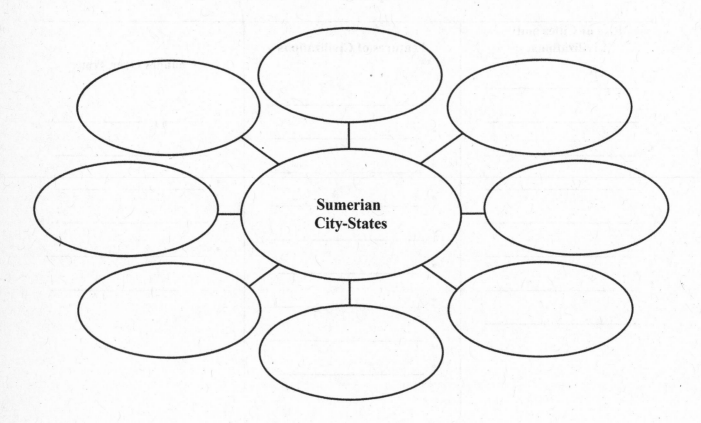

6. CIVILIZATION

As you read this section in your textbook, complete the following chart with details from the text to identify the main ideas about early civilizations.

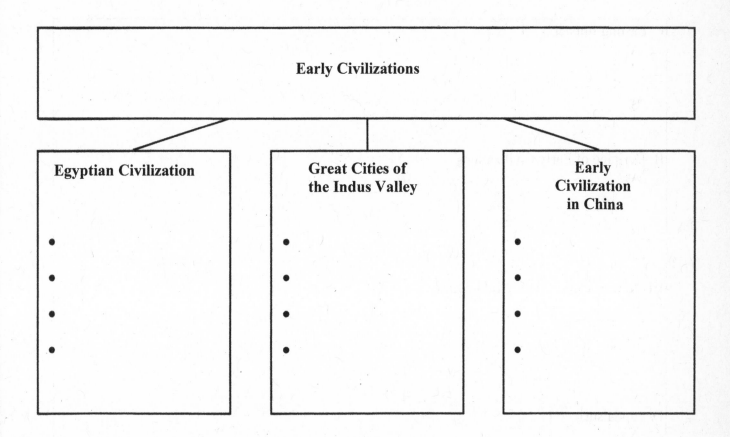

Early Civilizations

Egyptian Civilization

-
-
-
-

Great Cities of the Indus Valley

-
-
-

Early Civilization in China

-
-
-

7. THE HERITAGE OF THE RIVER VALLEY CIVILIZATIONS

As you read this section in your textbook, complete the following outline with details from the text to summarize the contributions of the river valley civilizations.

I. Lasting Impact
   A.
      1.
      2.
   B.
      1.
      2.

II. Heritage of Early Civilizations
   A.
      1.
      2.
   B.
      1.
      2.

III. New Societies in the Middle East
   A.
      1.
      2.
   B.
      1.
      2.

IV. Judaism
   A.
      1.
      2.
   B.
      1.
      2.

V. Assessing the Early Civilization Period
   A.
      1.
      2.
   B.
      1.
      2.

TERMS, PEOPLE, EVENTS

The following terms, people, and events are important to your understanding of the chapter. Write a brief definition of each.

Paleolithic Age

Homo sapiens

Neolithic Age

hunting and gathering

Bronze Age

slash and burn agriculture

civilization

Çatal Hüyük

nomads

Mesopotamia

Sumerians

Indus River valley

Harappa

Shang dynasty

MY KEY TERMS

Write down terms that are unfamiliar. How are the words used? Do other words or examples reveal their meaning? Try to figure out meaning from the context.

SHORT ANSWER REVIEW

Write the word or phrase that best completes the statement or answers the question.

1. Most civilizations developed writing, starting with the emergence of _____ in the Middle East around 3500 B.C.E.

2. It was under Babylonian rule that King _____ introduced the most famous early code of law.

3. By about 1500 B.C.E., a line of kings called the _____ ruled over early Chinese civilization.

4. A smaller regional group called the _____ devised an alphabet with 22 letters; this in turn was the ancestor of the Greek and Latin alphabets.

5. The largest city to develop along the Indus River was _____.

6. Early civilizations began in China along the _____ River.

7. The ancient civilization with the longest-lasting stability was in _____.

8. A large Neolithic village in modern Turkey, _____ was inhabited by 7000 B.C.E.

9. The belief in a single deity is known as _____.

10. The development of sedentary agriculture began is called the _____ revolution.

Choose the one alternative that best completes the statement or answers the question.

1. The human species was characterized in the Paleolithic Age by all of the following EXCEPT
a. the development of simple stone and wooden tools.
b. slow population growth.
c. the development of economies based on agriculture.
d. the ability to communicate with speech.

2. The characteristic political organization of the Tigris-Euphrates civilization was
a. democracy.
b. large, durable empires.
c. village-level government.
d. regional city-states.

3. Jewish monotheism
a. was spread actively by Jewish missionaries throughout the Middle East.
b. emphasized the power and abstraction of God.
c. included worship of various lesser gods.
d. emerged at the high point of Sumerian civilization.

4. The development of writing
a. resulted from new technologies, notably the invention of paper.
b. helps explain why agriculture could develop.
c. was necessary for the development of civilization.
d. facilitated the development of more formal and bureaucratic governments.

5. The concept of civilization includes all of the following EXCEPT:
a. greater social equality.
b. writing systems.
c. the development of cities.
d. political units capable of ruling large regions.

6. Egyptian civilization differed from Mesopotamian civilization by stressing
a. the use of slave labor.
b. more centralized government, that controlled the economy.
c. trade and science.
d. intense religious practice, tied to governmental structures.

7. As the most influential of the smaller Middle Eastern regional cultures, the Jewish culture differed from others most in its
a. monotheism.
b. strong military tradition.
c. large, centralized state.
d. vigorous sea trade.

8. A characteristic of the human species before the advent of civilization was
a. the ability to spread to various geographic settings and climate zones.
b. the ability to organize large political units.
c. the inability to communicate about abstractions such as death.
d. the ability to write and keep records of trade.

9. Which river valley civilization was most completely destroyed by invasion?
a. Huanghe
b. Amazon
c. Indus
d. Nile

10. The Neolithic Revolution refers to the period
a. in which democracy developed.
b. that saw the rise of settled agriculture.
c. before the full development of the *Homo sapiens* species.
d. before people learned to use fire.

After reading and studying the chapter, review your understanding by answering each of the following questions, which emphasize important ideas within the chapter.

1. What characteristics are associated with civilization?

2. Describe the culture of Paleolithic hunting and gathering societies.

3. How did the Neolithic revolution transform the material life and social organization of human communities?

4. Why did civilization begin in Mesopotamia?

5. What defined civilization in Sumerian culture?

6. What centers of civilization other than Egypt and Mesopotamia developed in the Middle East?

CHAPTER 2
Classical Civilization: China

Complete the following exercises in order *as you read* the chapter.

INTRODUCTION

Chapter introductions are a valuable guide to the material you are about to read, telling you what topics will be covered and how they fit together. If you keep the "big picture" provided by the introduction in mind as you read the chapter, you will find it much easier to organize your notes, identify important information, and avoid getting lost in the details. With this in mind, re-read the introduction to Chapter 2. As you read, make a list of the key topics you expect to learn about.

Key Topics

_____

_____

_____

_____

_____

_____

_____

_____

_____

_____

_____

_____

_____

_____

_____

_____

_____

_____

1. ESTABLISHMENT OF POLITICAL ORDER

As you read this section in your textbook, complete the following outline of the section to identify main ideas in each paragraph as well as the key words that inform those ideas.

I. Breakdown of dynastic control between 8th and 3rd centuries B.C.E.

    A.

        1.

        2.

    B.

        1.

        2.

II. Cultural Traditions

    A.

        1.

        2.

    B.

        1.

        2.

    C.

        1.

        2.

2. PATTERNS IN CLASSICAL CHINA

As you read this section in your textbook, complete the following outline of the section to sequence the important events in early China.

FOCUS QUESTION: *What characteristics defined the civilization that developed in China under its early rulers?*

I. The Zhou Dynasty
   A.
   B.
   C.
   D.
   E.
   F.
   G.
II. The Qin Dynasty
   A.
     1.
     2.
     3.
   B.
   C.
   D.
   E.
   F.
   E.
III. The Han Dynasty
   A.
   B.
   C.
   D.
   F.

Using the outline you completed, write a brief answer to the Focus Question.

3. POLITICAL INSTITUTIONS

As you read this section of your textbook, complete the following chart summarizing government traditions established during China's classical period.

Strong Bureaucracy	Role of the State
•	•
•	•
•	•
•	•
•	•

4. RELIGION AND CULTURE

As you read this section of your textbook, complete the following chart summarizing the political and social philosophy of Confucianism and Daoism.

Political and Social Philosophy	
Confucianism	**Daoism**
•	•
•	•
•	•
•	•
•	•

5. ECONOMY AND SOCIETY

As you read this section of your textbook, complete the following concept web summarizing the technological advances during the Han period.

FOCUS QUESTION: *How did the development of new technologies change Han society?*

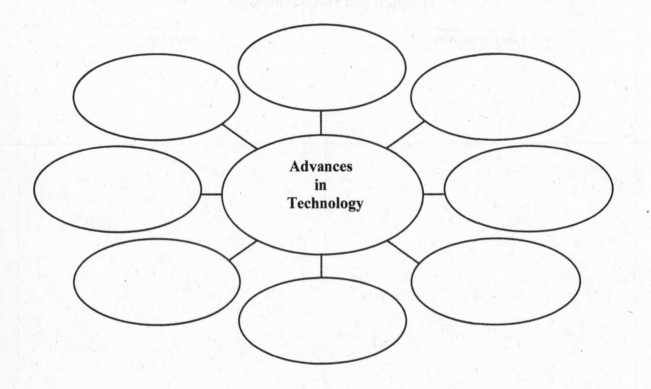

Using the information in your concept web, write a brief answer to the Focus Question.

TERMS, PEOPLE, EVENTS

The following terms, people, and events are important to your understanding of the chapter. Write a brief definition of each.

Zhou

Feudalism

Mandate of Heaven

Qin

Shi Huangdi

Warring States period

Confucius

Laozi

Daoism

Legalism

Great Wall

Han

MY KEY TERMS

Write down terms that are unfamiliar. How are the words used? Do other words or examples reveal their meaning? Try to figure out meaning from the context.

Write the word or phrase that best completes each statement or answers the question.

1. Families of kings, called _____, ruled over China during the classical period.

2. The Great Wall of China was built during the rule of the first emperor, _____.

3. The most famous ruler of the Han dynasty was _____.

4. Wu Ti set up a(n) _____ for all those who took exams to join the state bureaucracy.

5. The period when the Zhou dynasty disintegrated is called the _____.

6. During the Zhou dynasty, _____ traveled to many parts of China, preaching political virtue.

7. Confucian doctrine was recorded in a book called _____.

8. During the Qin and Han periods, an alternate system of political thought called _____ developed in China.

9. Daoism was spread in 5th-century China by the author _____.

10. Chinese art during the classical period stressed careful detail and _____.

MULTIPLE CHOICE REVIEW

Choose the one alternative that best completes the statement or answers the question.

1. One characteristic that differentiated classical civilizations from the earlier river valley societies was that
a. they were agricultural.
b. there was a higher rate of literacy.
c. there was less warfare.
d. they created larger political structures capable of controlling more territory.

2. A major factor in China's development of the first elaborate classical society was
a. a reduction in China's population.
b. a stable political leadership.
c. its ability to remain isolated and avoid outside invasion.
d. an absence of religious activity.

3. The Chinese view of nature stressed
a. harmony and balance.
b. a mystical belief that humans and nature were one.
c. the scientific control and domination of nature.
d. nature was determined by God.

4. Classical Chinese civilization was ruled by all of these EXCEPT
a. the Shang dynasty.
b. the Zhou dynasty.
c. the Qin dynasty.
d. the Han dynasty.

5. A distinguishing feature of the classical Chinese economy was
a. very little social stratification.
b. a series of international trading networks.
c. state support for merchant and artisan classes.
d. a high level of technology.

6. The Qin and Han dynasties were both characterized by
a. the formation of popular political parties.
b. increasing trade with the rest of the world.
c. a disdain for science and art.
d. powerful centralized governance.

7. The Qin dynasty was marked by all of the following EXCEPT
a. the decrease in power held by regional rulers and independent armies.
b. the building of the Great Wall of China.
c. an increase in the economic status of the peasant communities.
d. the incorporation of Hong Kong into the Chinese Empire.

8. China's classical period gave rise to all of the following intellectual traditions EXCEPT
a. Buddhism.
b. Daoism.
c. Legalism.
d. Confucianism.

9. Besides the "mean people," which of the following groups was considered to have the least status in classical China?
a. Merchants
b. Peasants
c. Philosophers
d. Artisans

10. All of the following constituted a function of the state in Han China EXCEPT
a. attack on local warrior landlords.
b. civil service examinations.
c. promoting Confucian philosophy.
d. detachment from the lives of the Chinese masses.

READING CHECK: MAKING CONNECTIONS

After reading and studying the chapter, review your understanding by answering each of the following questions, which emphasize important ideas within the chapter.

1. Describe Confucius' political philosophy.

2. Describe the Daoist alternative to Confucian political and social philosophy.

3. What was the significance of the Qin dynasty?

4. How did the Han institutionalize Confucian political philosophy?

5. What circumstances led to the overthrow of the Han in 9 C.E. and 220 C.E.?

Classical Civilization: India

Complete the following exercises in order *as you read* the chapter.

INTRODUCTION

Chapter introductions are a valuable guide to the material you are about to read, telling you what topics will be covered and how they fit together. If you keep the "big picture" provided by the introduction in mind as you read the chapter, you will find it much easier to organize your notes, identify important information, and avoid getting lost in the details. With this in mind, re-read the introduction to Chapter 3. As you read, make a list of the key topics you expect to learn about.

Key Topics

_____

_____

_____

_____

_____

_____

_____

_____

_____

_____

_____

_____

_____

_____

_____

_____

_____

_____

_____

_____

1. THE FRAMEWORK FOR INDIAN HISTORY: GEOGRAPHY AND A FORMATIVE PERIOD

As you read this section in your textbook, complete the following outline of the section to identify main ideas in each paragraph as well as the key words that inform those ideas.

FOCUS QUESTION: *How did geography give rise to India's distinctive culture?*

I. Formative Influences
  A. Geography
    1.
    2.
  B. Topography
    1.
    2.
    3.
      a.
      b.
      c.
    4.
  C. Climate
    1.
    2.

Using the information in your outline, write a brief answer to the Focus Question.

2. THE FRAMEWORK FOR INDIAN HISTORY: GEOGRAPHY AND A FORMATIVE PERIOD

As you read this section in your textbook, complete the following concept web to summarize the main aspects of the Aryan civilization.

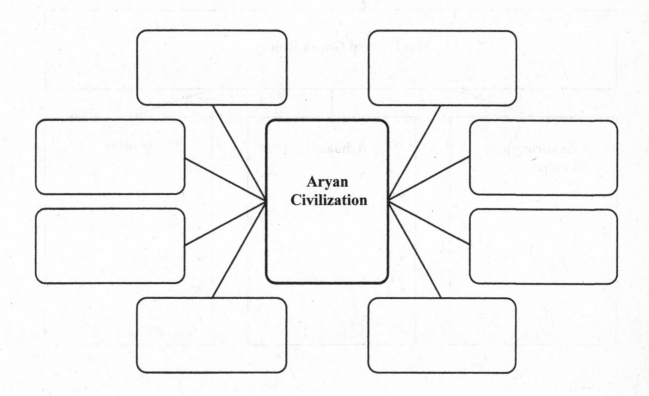

3. PATTERNS IN CLASSICAL INDIA

As you read this section in your textbook, complete the following chart to summarize important events in the Maurya and Gupta periods.

FOCUS QUESTION: *What was the impact of Maurya and Gupta rulers on the development of India during the classic era?*

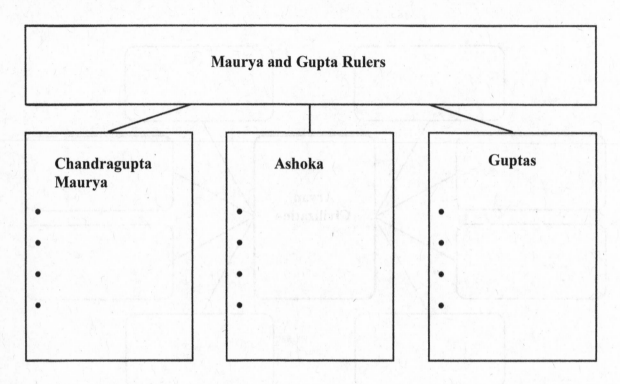

Maurya and Gupta Rulers		
Chandragupta Maurya	**Ashoka**	**Guptas**
•	•	•
•	•	•
•	•	•
•	•	•

Using the information in your chart, write a brief answer to the Focus Question.

4. POLITICAL INSTITUTIONS

As you read this section in your textbook, complete the following concept web to detail the main characteristics of the caste system.

FOCUS QUESTION: *How did India's caste system develop after the Epic Age?*

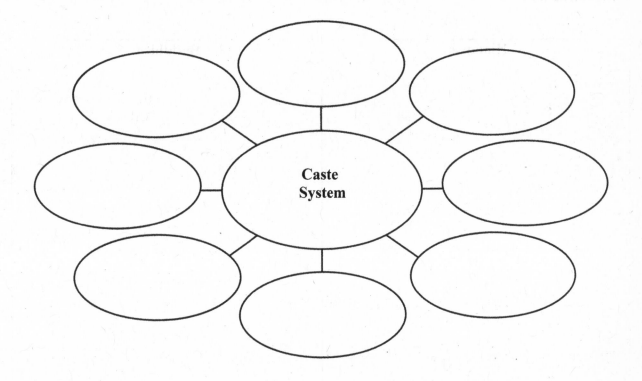

Caste
System

Using the information in your concept web, write a brief answer to the Focus Question.

5. RELIGION AND CULTURE

As you read this section in your textbook, complete the following chart to summarizing the origins and traditions of Hinduism and Buddhism.

FOCUS QUESTION: *What were the chief differences between Buddhism and the developing Hindu tradition?*

Hinduism	Buddhism
•	•
•	•
•	•
•	•
•	•

Using the information in your chart, write a brief answer to the Focus Question.

6. ECONOMY AND SOCIETY

As you read this section in your textbook, complete the following concept web to identify the characteristics of family life in India during the classic era.

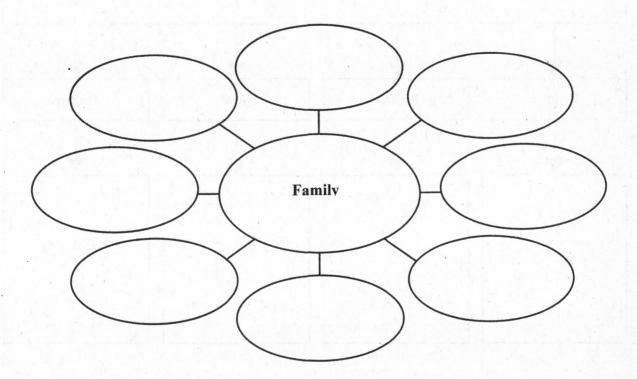

7. INDIAN INFLUENCE AND COMPARATIVE FEATURES

As you read this section in your textbook, complete the following chart comparing classical civilization in India and China.

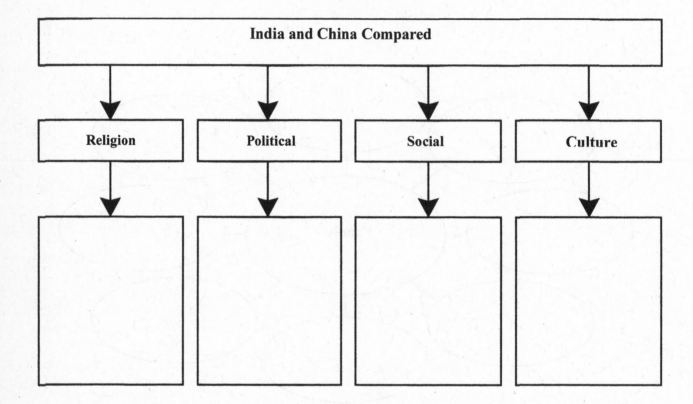

TERMS, PEOPLE, EVENTS

The following terms, people, and events are important to your understanding of the chapter. Write a brief definition of each.

Buddha	reincarnation
Alexander the Great	nirvana
Himalayan Mountains	*Kamasutra*
Aryans	scholar-gentry
Sanskrit	Shiva
Vedas	Vishnu
Mahabharata	
Ramayana	
Upanishads	
Varnas	
Untouchables	
Indra	
Chandragupta Maurya	
Maurya dynasty	
Ashoka	
Dharma	
Gupta dynasty	
Kautilya	
gurus	
Karma	

MY KEY TERMS

Write down terms that are unfamiliar. How are the words used? Do other words or examples reveal their meaning? Try to figure out meaning from the context.

Write the word or phrase that best completes each statement or answers the question.

1. The vast Indian subcontinent is partially separated from the rest of Asia by northern mountain ranges, most notably the _____.

2. During the Vedic and Epic ages, the _____ conquerors impressed their stamp on Indian society.

3. Early literary epics developed by the Aryans were passed on orally and written down in the language called _____.

4. The Indian emperor _____ was the best-known Mauryan leader.

5. The dynasty that followed the Maurya, the _____, featured a long era of political stability.

6. The priestly caste, or _____, stood at the top of India's caste system.

7. Unlike other major world religions, _____ had no single founder or central holy figure.

8. The Hindu ethical code, or _____, was far less detailed than the ethical codes of other major religions.

9. These southern Indians, the _____, were active in trading networks all over Asia.

10. Toward the end of the Epic Age, _____ built on the foundation of Hinduism to create another major world religion.

Choose the one alternative that best completes the statement or answers the question.

1. All of the following defined the Vedic and Epic ages in India EXCEPT
a. the development of Sanskrit.
b. an early form of a caste system.
c. consistently high levels of agricultural output.
d. the rise of Buddhism.

2. The first ruler of the Maurya dynasty was
A) Ashoka.
B) Alexander the Great.
C) Chandragupta.
D) Kanishka.

3. The Maurya dynasty differed from the Gupta dynasty in that
a. it was imposed by Aryan conquerors.
b. it ruled a larger territory.
c. it attacked Buddhist beliefs.
d. it refused to develop a strong army.

4. Classical India's political climate was characterized most by
a. a politically astute population.
b. an array of regional political cultures.
c. a highly-centralized government.
d. democratic institutions.

5. The Indian caste system influenced the Indian governmental system by
a. enforcing rules about social behavior.
b. unifying the subcontinent under a single government.
c. creating a widespread interest in constitutional issues.
d. promoting a belief in individual rights.

6. Hinduism was defined by all of the following EXCEPT
a. it was the religion of India's majority.
b. it lacked a central deity.
c. it held a belief in reincarnation.
d. it excluded all other religions.

7. Buddhism differs from Hinduism by not believing in
a. a caste system.
b. holy leaders.
c. nirvana.
d. the importance of moral obligations.

8. Indian trading networks expanded to include all of the following EXCEPT
a. the Middle East.
b. China.
c. Sri Lanka.
d. Russia.

9. In contrast to China, India
a. had more direct contact with other societies and civilizations.
b. demonstrated a restrained artistic style.
c. lacked regional diversity.
d. had a more flexible social order.

10. In contrast to those in China, the values developed in classical India
a. promoted considerable equality between men and women.
b. led to the evolution and prominence of several distinct religions.
c. urged that children not be required to work.
d. encouraged greater emotional spontaneity.

READING REVIEW: MAKING CONNECTIONS

After reading and studying the chapter, review your understanding by answering each of the following questions, which emphasize important ideas within the chapter.

1. Why did the caste system develop and how was it perpetuated?

2. How did Buddhism influence Asoka's rule?

3. What were some of the advances of the Gupta dynasty?

4. How was Aryan society organized?

Classical Civilization in the Mediterranean and Middle East

Complete the following exercises in order *as you read* the chapter.

INTRODUCTION

Chapter introductions are a valuable guide to the material you are about to read, telling you what topics will be covered and how they fit together. If you keep the "big picture" provided by the introduction in mind as you read the chapter, you will find it much easier to organize your notes, identify important information, and avoid getting lost in the details. With this in mind, re-read the introduction to Chapter 4. As you read, make a list of the key topics you expect to learn about.

Key Topics

_____

_____

_____

_____

_____

_____

_____

_____

_____

_____

_____

_____

_____

_____

_____

_____

_____

_____

_____

_____

1. THE PERSIAN EMPIRE: A NEW PERSPECTIVE IN THE MIDDLE EAST

As you read this section of your textbook, complete the outline summarizing the political and cultural aspects of the Persian Empire.

FOCUS QUESTION: *What traditions helped shape the Persian Empire's strong political and cultural presence?*

I. Political Styles and Innovations
   A. Persian Politics
      1.
      2.
   B. Persian Leaders
      1.
      2.
         a.
         b.
         c.
         d.
   C. Religious Influence
      1.
         a.
         b.
         c.
      2.
         a.
         b.
         c.
      3.
         a.
         b.
   D.
   E.
         a.
         b.
         c.
         d.

Using the information in your outline, write a brief answer to the Focus Question.

2. PATTERNS OF GREEK AND ROMAN HISTORY

As you read this section of your textbook, complete the outline summarizing the rapid rise of civilization in Greece.

FOCUS QUESTION: *What are the characteristics of city-states?*

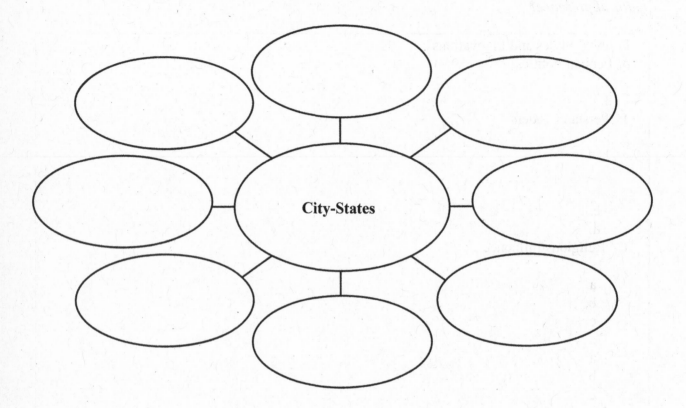

Using the information in your concept web, write a brief answer to the Focus Question.

3. PATTERNS OF GREEK AND ROMAN HISTORY

As you read this section, complete the flowchart below to identify causes and effects of important events during the Roman republic.

FOCUS QUESTION: *What values formed the basis of Roman society and government?*

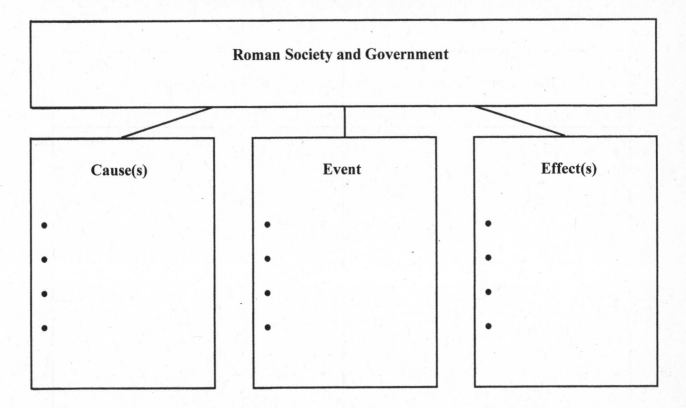

Roman Society and Government

Cause(s)

-
-
-
-

Event

-
-
-
-

Effect(s)

-
-
-
-

Using the information in your chart, write a brief answer to the Focus Question.

4. PATTERNS OF GREEK AND ROMAN HISTORY

As you read this section in your textbook, complete the following chart to recognize the causes that led to the decline of the Roman republic and the rise of the Roman empire.

FOCUS QUESTION: *What factors led to the decline of the Roman republic and the rise of the Roman Empire?*

Decline of the Republic	Rise of the Empire
•	•
•	•
•	•
•	•

Using the information in your chart, write a brief answer to the Focus Question.

5. Patterns of Greek and Roman History

As you read this section in your textbook, complete the chart below to list the causes of the fall of the western Roman empire.

FOCUS QUESTION: *How did military, political, social, and economic factors combine to cause the fall of the western Roman empire?*

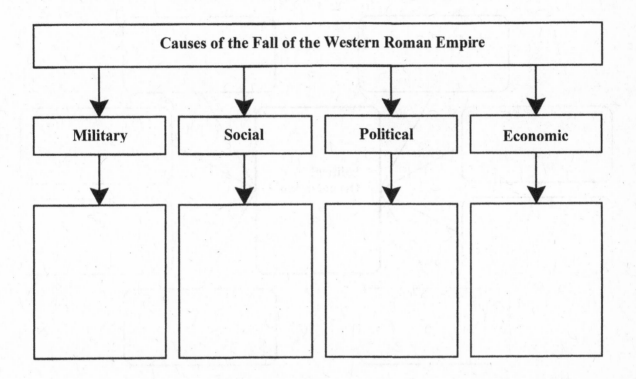

Causes of the Fall of the Western Roman Empire

| Military | Social | Political | Economic |

Using the information in your chart, write a brief answer to the Focus Question.

6. GREEK AND ROMAN POLITICAL INSTITUTIONS

As you read this section in your textbook, complete the chart below identifying the characteristics of the political organization of Greek civilization.

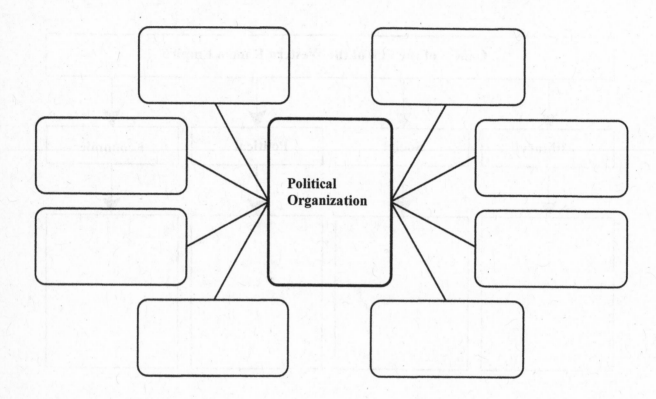

7. RELIGION AND CULTURE

As you read this section in your textbook, complete the chart below to record the supporting details about Greek achievements discussed in the section.

FOCUS QUESTION: *How did Greek thinkers, artists, and writers explore the nature of the universe and people's place in it?*

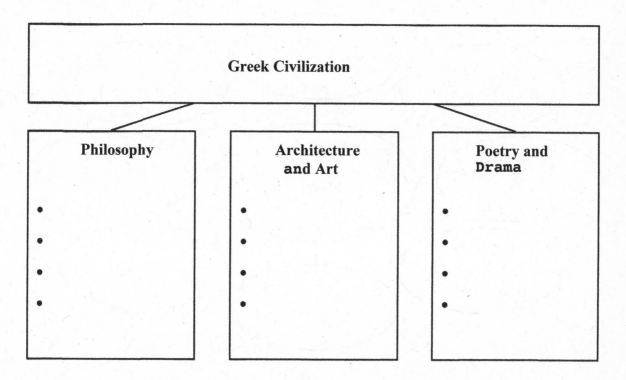

Using the information in your chart, write a brief answer to the Focus Question.

8. ECONOMY AND SOCIETY IN THE MEDITERRANEAN

As you read this section of your textbook, complete the outline summarizing slavery in Greek civilization.

FOCUS QUESTION: *What was the role of slavery in the Greek economy and culture?*

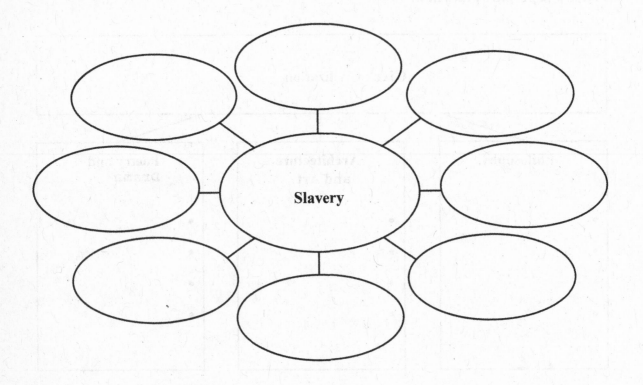

Slavery

Using the information in your concept web, write a brief answer to the Focus Question.

TERMS, PEOPLE, EVENTS

The following terms, people, and events are important to your understanding of the chapter. Define each one.

Cyrus the Great	Socrates
Zoroastrianism	Iliad
Pericles	Odyssey
Philip II	
Hellenistic period	
Roman Republic	
Punic Wars	
Hannibal	
Carthage	
Julius Caesar	
Augustus Caesar	
Diocletian	
Constantine	
polis	
direct democracy	
Senate	
consuls	
Cicero	
Aristotle	
Stoics	
Doric	
Ionic	
Corinthian	

MY KEY TERMS

Write down terms that are unfamiliar. How are the words used? Do other words or examples reveal their meaning? Try to figure out meaning from the context.

Write the word or phrase that best completes each statement or answers the question.

1. Athens and _____ emerged as the two leading city-states in classical Greece.

2. _____ created an empire based on Greek culture through the Middle East into India, setting the stage for the Hellenistic era.

3. Roman conquest spread to north Africa after defeating Carthage in the _____ Wars.

4. The word "politics" comes from the Greek word for city-state, _____.

5. The best-known law code of the Roman republic was the _____.

6. The Athenian philosopher _____ encouraged his students to question conventional wisdom and was put to death for this teaching.

7. Greek mathematicians made especially groundbreaking advances in the field of _____.

8. The Athenian dramatist_____ wrote plays like *Oedipus Rex* that revealed the psychological flaws of the principal character.

9. The two leaders of the executive branch of Rome's republic were called _____.

10. _____ gained control of Rome and effectively ended the republic era.

MULTIPLE CHOICE REVIEW

Choose the one alternative that best completes the statement or answers the question.

1. The Greek genius was in democracy; the Roman genius was in
a. engineering.
b. politics.
c. democracy.
d. philosophy.

2. The quintessential Greek political institution was
a. imperial rule
b. monarchy.
c. the democratic city-state.
d. a feudal social order.

3. The Roman Empire
a. disallowed the use of slaves.
b. prevented foreigners from trading within the empire.
c. set up a military draft to supply the army.
d. generally tolerated local politicians and religions.

4. The senate of republican Rome consisted of what group?
a. Landed aristocracy
b. Emperors
c. Urban workers
d. Merchants and businessmen

5. The most characteristic political form in the classical Mediterranean world was
a. tyranny.
b. direct democracy.
c. representative democracy.
d. aristocratic democracy.

6. Classical Mediterranean society differed from classical China in all of the following ways EXCEPT that the Mediterranean society used
a. a more elaborate legal framework.
b. the idea of active citizenship.
c. the same trade routes.
d. a diversity of political systems.

7. This Greek philosopher believed humans could approach an understanding of the perfect forms of the absolute true, good, and beautiful.
a. Socrates
b. Plato
c. Aristotle
d. Pericles

8. The Greeks made especially notable advances in
a. science.
b. literature.
c. weaponry.
d. religious thought.

9. From a Confucian viewpoint, the Roman Empire might have been criticized for placing too much confidence in
a. divine backing for the emperor.
b. public works functions for the masses.
c. education of leaders.
d. laws rather than trained officials.

10. Roman slaves were used in all of the following EXCEPT
a. work in the mines.
b. agricultural labor.
c. household care.
d. military service.

READING REVIEW: MAKING CONNECTIONS

After reading and studying the chapter, review your understanding by answering each of the following questions, which emphasize important ideas within the chapter.

1. How did the Greek city-states work together? Why were they often separate?

2. What was the function of philosophy in Greek culture?

3. Compare and contrast Greek civilization to Roman civilization.

4. Compare and contrast Greek and Roman culture.

5. Describe the constitution of the Roman Empire.

CHAPTER 5
The Classical Period: Directions, Diversities, and Declines by 500 C.E.

Complete the following exercises in order *as you read* the chapter.

INTRODUCTION

Chapter introductions are a valuable guide to the material you are about to read, telling you what topics will be covered and how they fit together. If you keep the "big picture" provided by the introduction in mind as you read the chapter, you will find it much easier to organize your notes, identify important information, and avoid getting lost in the details. With this in mind, re-read the introduction to Chapter 5. As you read, make a list of the key topics you expect to learn about.

Key Topics

_____

_____

_____

_____

_____

_____

_____

_____

_____

_____

_____

_____

_____

_____

_____

_____

_____

1. EXPANSION AND INTEGRATION

As you read this section in your textbook, complete the outline to identify the main ideas about territorial expansion and integration in classical civilization.

I. Expansion and Integration

  A.

     1.

     2.

     3.

  B.

     1.

     2.

     3.

  C.

     1.

     2.

  D.

     1.

        a.

        b.

        c.

        d.

     2.

        a.

        b.

        c.

        d.

2. DECLINE IN CHINA AND INDIA

As you read this section in your textbook, complete the chart below to summarize the main ideas identifying the decline of the Han and Gupta empires.

Collapse of the Han Dynasty	End of the Gupta Empire
•	•
•	•
•	•
•	•
•	•

3. DECLINE AND FALL IN ROME

As you read this section in your textbook, complete the chart below to list the causes of the fall of the Roman Empire.

FOCUS QUESTION: *How did military, political, social, and economic factors combine to cause the fall of the Roman Empire?*

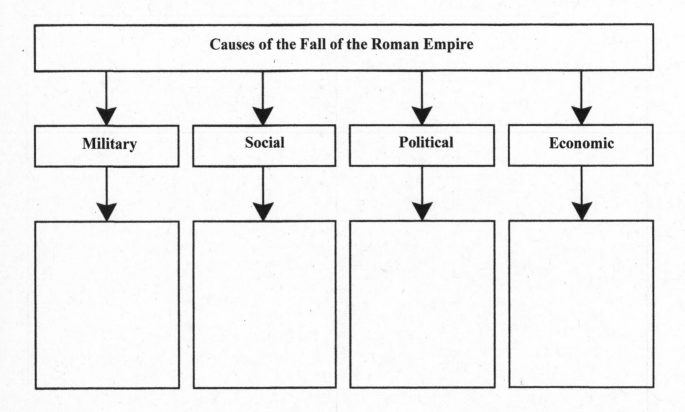

Causes of the Fall of the Roman Empire

Military	Social	Political	Economic

Using the information in your chart, write a brief answer to the Focus Question.

4. THE NEW RELIGIOUS MAP

As you read this section of your textbook, complete the table below to show the factors that caused the rise of Christianity and its establishment as the official religion of the Roman Empire.

FOCUS QUESTION: *How did Christianity emerge and then spread to become the official religion in Rome?*

Causes	Effects
•	**Rise of Christianity**
•	•
•	•
•	•
•	•
•	**Establishment of Christianity as the empire's official religion**
•	•
•	•
•	•

Using the information in your chart, write a brief answer to the Focus Question.

TERMS, EVENTS, PEOPLE

The following terms, people, and events are important to your understanding of the chapter. Define each one.

Axum	Mahayana
Shinto	Bodhisattvas
Celts	Saints
Slavs	Pope
Olmec	Augustine
Polynesia	Benedict
Yellow	Turbans
Tang	
Rajput	
Allah	
Diocletian	
Constantine	
Byzantine Empire	

MY KEY TERMS

Write down terms that are unfamiliar. How are the words used? Do other words or examples reveal their meaning? Try to figure out meaning from the context.

SHORT ANSWER REVIEW

Write the word or phrase that best completes each statement or answers the question.

1. By about 1000 B.C.E., the kingdom of _____ existed along the upper Nile, possessed a form of writing adapted from hieroglyphics, and mastered the use of iron.

2. Japan's prominent religion, _____, provided for worship of political rulers and the spirits of nature.

3. The first civilization in Central America, the _____, passed on many of its features to its successor civilizations.

4. Attacks by the _____ from central Asia led to the decline of classical civilizations.

5. During the decline of the Han dynasty, Daoist leaders called the _____ promised a golden age to be brought by divine magic.

6. The eastern part of the Roman Empire was based in the city of _____.

7. The last effort to restore Mediterranean unity came under the Byzantine emperor _____.

8. Centuries after the Buddha's death, the doctrine of _____ arose, claiming that some people could gain nirvana through their own meditation.

9. An east Asian form of Buddhism, _____, or the Mahayana, retained basic Buddhist beliefs.

10. The Christian institution of organized monasticism was first developed by _____.

Choose the one alternative that best completes the statement or answers the question.

1. Civilizations developed independently from the three classical civilizations in
a. northeast Africa.
b. Japan.
c. the Americas.
d. Korea.

2. Which of these belief systems saw a change in the perception of its founder from a teacher of ethics into a messiah?
a. Hinduism
b. Buddhism
c. Christianity
d. Daoism

3. The decline of the three classical civilizations between 200 and 600 C.E. were all characterized by
a. outside invasions.
b. spread of disease.
c. rise of Christianity.
d. retained strength of governments.

4. One important early symptom of Rome's decline was
a. individuals' lack of interest in being emperor.
b. the use of slave labor.
c. the replacement of republican rule by empire.
d. the drop in population.

5. The first kingdoms in Africa below the Sahara showed the influence of
a. Egypt and Hellenism.
b. Rome and Phoenicia.
c. Indian merchants.
d. east Asia.

6. The end of the Gupta Empire differed from the decline of Rome in that it did NOT involve
a. a change in political institutions.
b. outside invasion.
c. the introduction of a new religion.
d. the weakening of central government.

7. Despite major differences, Christianity, Hinduism, and Buddhism all emphasized
a. a strong priesthood.
b. clearly organized church structures.
c. hostility to worship of religious images.
d. life after death.

8. Compared with Hinduism, Christianity is more likely to
a. disapprove of other belief systems.
b. have a disorganized church structure.
c. see nature as superior to humans.
d. believe women are morally superior to men.

9. The eastern portion of the Roman Empire experienced less decline than the West for all the following reasons EXCEPT
a. the eastern portion had older traditions of civilization.
b. many of the symptoms of decline were in the West.
c. the East faced less pressure from barbarian invasions.
d. the East resisted the spread of Christianity.

10. Which of these was NOT a domesticated animal in the Americas in this era?
a. The turkey
b. The horse
c. The guinea pig
d. The dog

READING REVIEW: MAKING CONNECTIONS

After reading and studying the chapter, review your understanding by answering each of the following questions, which emphasize important ideas within the chapter.

1. What were the main factors in Rome's decline? Which do you judge most important? Why?

2. Compare the major beliefs and religious organization of Christianity and Buddhism.

3. Taking into account both Egypt and Kush, what were the main features of civilization in Africa prior to the first century C.E.?

4. How did the territorial expansion of the republic affect the society and politics of Rome?

5. Why did Christianity spread within the Roman Empire?

CHAPTER 6
The First Global Civilization: The Rise and Spread of Islam

Complete the following exercises in order *as you read* the chapter.

INTRODUCTION

Chapter introductions are a valuable guide to the material you are about to read, telling you what topics will be covered and how they fit together. If you keep the "big picture" provided by the introduction in mind as you read the chapter, you will find it much easier to organize your notes, identify important information, and avoid getting lost in the details. With this in mind, re-read the introduction to Chapter 6. As you read, make a list of the key topics you expect to learn about.

Key Topics

_____

_____

_____

_____

_____

_____

_____

_____

_____

_____

_____

_____

_____

_____

_____

_____

_____

_____

1. DESERT AND TOWN: THE PRE-ISLAMIC ARABIAN WORLD

As you read this section in your textbook, complete the outline below with the main ideas about Arab social organization.

I. Desert and Town: The Pre-Islamic Arabian World
  A.
    1.

    2.

  B.
    1.

    2.

    3.

    4.

  C.
    1.

    2.

    3.

    4.

  D.
    1.

    2.

  E.
    1.

    2.

2. THE LIFE OF MUHAMMAD AND THE GENESIS OF ISLAM

As you read this section in your textbook, complete the timeline to record the sequence of events in Muhammad's life; then complete the chart that follows to identify the teachings of Islam.

Timeline of Muhammad's Life

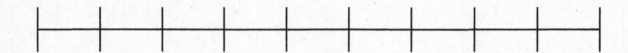

3. THE LIFE OF MUHAMMAD AND THE GENESIS OF ISLAM

As you read this section in your textbook, complete the chart that follows to identify the teachings of Islam.

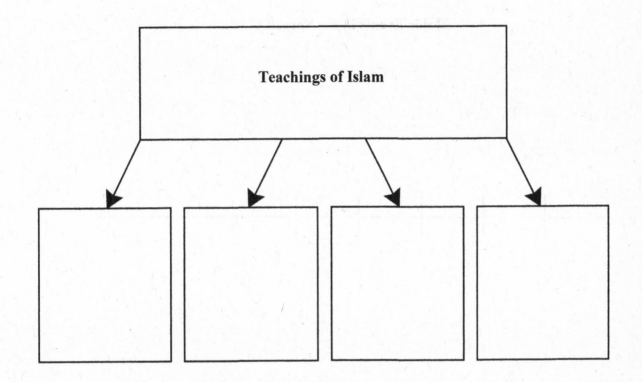

4. THE ARAB EMPIRE OF THE UMAYYADS

As you read the section in your textbook, complete the following timeline to record the major events in the spread of Islam and the rise and fall of Muslim empires.

FOCUS QUESTION: *How did Muhammad's successors extend Muslim rule and spread Islam?*

Major Events in the Spread of Islam

Using the information in your timeline, write a brief answer to the Focus Question.

5. THE ARAB EMPIRE OF THE UMAYYADS AND FROM ARAB TO ISLAMIC EMPIRE: THE EARLY ABBASID ERA

As you read these sections in your textbook, complete the following chart to record the main ideas about the Abbasid and Umayyad Empires.

FOCUS QUESTION: *What was the difference between the Abbasid Empire and the Umayyad Empire?*

Umayyad Empire	Abbasid Empire
•	•
•	•
•	•
•	•

Using the information in your chart, write a brief answer to the Focus Question.

6. FROM ARAB TO ISLAMIC EMPIRE: THE EARLY ABBASID ERA

As you read these sections in your textbook, complete the following chart to categorize advances made during the golden age of Islamic civilization.

Economics	•
	•
	•
	•
Art	•
	•
	•
Philosophy	•
	•
	•
Science	•
	•
	•

CHAPTER REVIEW

TERMS, EVENTS, PEOPLE

The following terms, people, and events are important to your understanding of the chapter. Define each one.

Bedouin

Shaykhs

Mecca

Umayyad

Ka'ba

Qur'an

Umma

Zakat

Five pillars

Caliph

Ali

Abu Bakr

Ridda Wars

Jihad

Battle of Siffin

Sunni

Shi'a

Karbala

Mawali

Dhimmis

Abbasids

Wazir

Ayan

Allah

Khadijah

Hijra

Ramadam

Hajj

Damascus

Hadiths

Battle of River Zab

Baghdad

Dhows

Mosque

MY KEY TERMS

Write down terms that are unfamiliar. How are the words used? Do other words or examples reveal their meaning? Try to figure out meaning from the context.

Write the word or phrase that best completes the statement or answers the question.

1. The _____ were tribal and clan leaders within bedouin society.

2. The site of the Ka'ba and original home of Muhammad, _____, was located in the mountainous region along the Red Sea on the Arabian Peninsula.

3. The clan within the Quraysh that controlled the political and commercial life of Mecca was the _____.

4. The Prophet of Islam was _____, whose revelations were recorded in the Qur'an.

5. The obligatory religious duties of all Muslims, the _____, were profession of the faith, prayer, fasting during Ramadan, zakat, and hajj.

6. The _____ was the religious and political leader in Islam after the death of Muhammad.

7. _____ was the concept of Islamic holy war.

8. The capital of the Umayyad Empire was at _____.

9. _____ were literally "people of the book," usually either Christians or Jews.

10. The dynasty that followed the Umayyad was the _____ dynasty.

MULTIPLE CHOICE REVIEW

Choose the one alternative that best completes the statement or answers the question.

1. Which of the following was *NOT* a feature of the first millennium of Islamic civilization
a. key links and channels for trade and cultural exchange in the Eastern Hemisphere
b. transfer of food crops between regions
c. destruction of the urban centers of classical civilization
d. study and preservation of the learning of ancient civilization

2. What was the basic social group of the Bedouin in pre-Islamic society?
a. large tribal confederations
b. hunting and gathering bands
c. kin-related clan groups
d. nuclear households

3. What clan was responsible for the foundation of Mecca?
a. Umayyad
b. Abbasid
c. Aghlabid
d. Tulunid

4. Prior to Muhammad's revelations, the religion of most Bedouin clans was
a. primarily Christian.
b. primarily Judaic.
c. a mixture of animism and polytheism.
d. closely related to that of the Brahmans.

5. The religious shrine that served as the focal point for rituals in pre-Islamic Mecca was the
a. Karbala.
b. Yathrib.
c. Hijra.
d. Ka'ba.

6. Which of the following statements concerning Muhammad's flight to Medina is *NOT* correct?
a. He fled because of the threat of assassination in Mecca.
b. He fled because he was invited to mediate a dispute among the tribes of Medina.
c. Muhammad fled from Mecca with nearly one quarter of the city's population.
d. Once in Medina, he attracted new followers to his faith.

7. The Islamic umma was
a. the concept of community of the faithful that transcended clan boundaries.
b. the holy book into which Muhammad's revelations were recorded.
c. the principle of succession following the death of Muhammad.
d. the name given to Muhammad's flight from Mecca to Medina.

8. The Ridda Wars were fought
a. to suppress rival prophets and to restore the unity of Islam.
b. between the supporters of Ali and the Umayyad clan.
c. between the supporters of Husayn, Ali's son, and the Umayyad caliph.
d. to overthrow the Umayyad dynasty.

9. What was the nature of citizenship within the Umayyad Empire?
a. All converts to Islam, regardless of ethnic origin, were full citizens and members of the elite.
b. Only Muslim Arabs were first-class citizens.
c. The Umayyads recognized the empire's residents, whether Muslims or *people of the book*, as full citizens.
d. Arabs rapidly lost their dominance in the Umayyad Empire to the native residents of Persia.

10. Unlike the Umayyad Empire, the Abbasid Empire
a. practiced absolutism.
b. admitted the *mawali* as full members of the Islamic community.
c. freed all slaves.
d. persecuted the Shi'is.

READING REVIEW: MAKING CONNECTIONS

After reading and studying the chapter, review your understanding by answering each of the following questions, which emphasize important ideas within the chapter.

1. What was the nature of Bedouin society prior to Muhammad's revelations?

2. How did Islam address fundamental problems in Arabic society?

3. What was the nature and extent of the Umayyad Empire?

4. What event led to the fall of the Umayyads?

5. How was the Abbasid Empire different from the Umayyad Empire?

CHAPTER 7
Abbasid Decline and the Spread of Islamic Civilization to South and Southeast Asia

Complete the following exercises in order *as you read* the chapter.

INTRODUCTION

Chapter introductions are a valuable guide to the material you are about to read, telling you what topics will be covered and how they fit together. If you keep the "big picture" provided by the introduction in mind as you read the chapter, you will find it much easier to organize your notes, identify important information, and avoid getting lost in the details. With this in mind, re-read the introduction to Chapter 7. As you read, make a list of the key topics you expect to learn about.

Key Topics

_____

_____

_____

_____

_____

_____

_____

_____

_____

_____

_____

_____

_____

_____

_____

_____

_____

_____

1. THE ISLAMIC HEARTLANDS IN THE MIDDLE AND LATE ABBASID ERAS

As you read this section in your textbook, complete the outline below with the main ideas Islamic Heartlands during the Middle and late Abbasid Eras.

I. Imperial Extravagance and Succession Disputes
   A.
   B.
   C.
   D.

II. Imperial Breakdown and Agrarian Disorder
   A.
   B.
      1.
      2.

III. The Declining Position of Women in the Family and Society
   A.
      1.
      2.
   B.
      1.
      2.

IV. Nomadic Incursions and the Eclipse of Caliphal Power
   A.
   B.
      1.
      2.
      3

V. The Impact of the Christian Crusades
   A.
      1.
      2.
      3.
   B.
      1.
      2.
      3.

2. THE ISLAMIC HEARTLANDS IN THE MIDDLE AND LATE ABBASID ERAS

As you read this section in your textbook, complete the chart below with the main ideas about the declining position of women during the Abbasid era.

FOCUS QUESTION: *What was the position of women in the Abbasid Empire?*

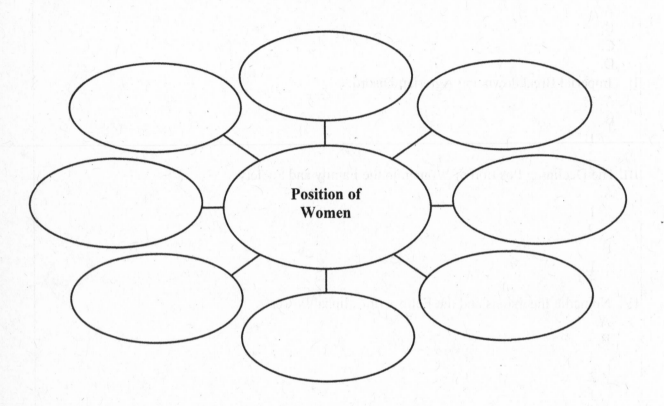

Using the information in your concept web, write a brief answer to the Focus Question.

3. AN AGE OF LEARNING AND ARTISTIC REFINEMENTS

As you read this section in your textbook, complete the chart below with the main ideas about Persian literature and achievement in the sciences.

Persian Literature	Achievements in Science
•	•
•	•
•	•
•	•

4. AN AGE OF LEARNING AND ARTISTIC REFINEMENTS

As you read this section in your textbook, complete the chart below with the main ideas about Sufism.

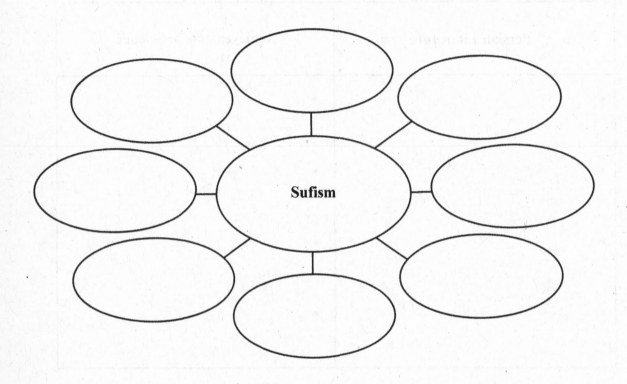

5. THE COMING OF ISLAM TO SOUTH ASIA

As you read this section in your textbook, complete the chart below with the main ideas about Indian influences on Islamic civilization.

FOCUS QUESTION: *What were key Indian influences on Islamic civilization after the conquest of Sind?*

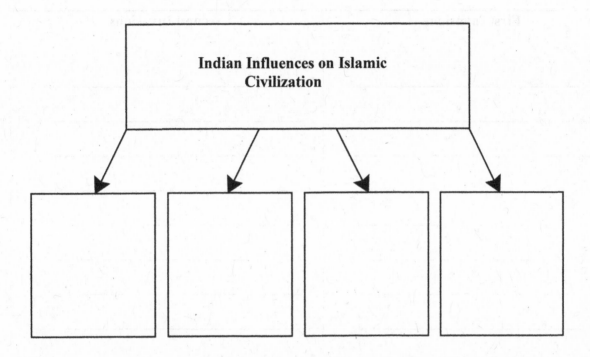

Using the information in your chart, write a brief answer to the Focus Question.

6. THE COMING OF ISLAM TO SOUTH ASIA

As you read this section in your textbook, complete the chart below with the main ideas about the first and second wave of Muslim invasions.

Muslim Invasions	
First Invasions	**Second Invasions**
• _____ _____ • _____ _____ • _____ _____ • _____ _____ • _____ _____	• _____ _____ • _____ _____ • _____ _____ • _____ _____ • _____ _____

7. THE COMING OF ISLAM TO SOUTH ASIA

After reading this section of your textbook, insert the following events into the timeline. This will help you to compare important historical events chronologically.

Events

Buyids capture Baghdad	establishment of Delhi sultanate
crusaders capture Jerusalem	first Muslim raids into India
introduction of Islam into southeast Asia	Mongols capture Baghdad

Dates

1290s C.E.
711 C.E.
945 C.E.
1099 C.E.
1206 C.E.
1258 C.E.

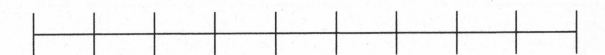

8. THE SPREAD OF ISLAM TO SOUTHEAST ASIA

As you read this section in your textbook, complete the chart below with the main ideas about how Islam spread to Southeast Asia.

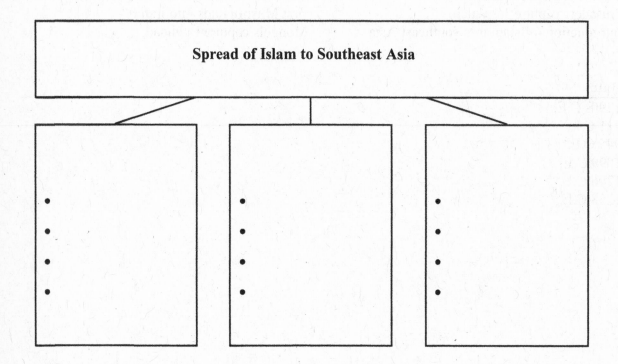

TERMS, EVENTS, PEOPLE

The following terms, people, and events are important to your understanding of the chapter. Define each one.

Harun al-Rashid

Buyids

Seljuk Turks

Crusades

Saladin

Ibn Khaldun

Rubaiyat

Sufis

Mongols

Muhammad ibn Qasim

Harsha

Sati

Bhaktic cults

Kabir

Sultan

Holy Land

Chinggis Khan

Mamluks

Rajas

Sultans of Delhi

MY KEY TERMS

Write down terms that are unfamiliar. How are the words used? Do other words or examples reveal their meaning? Try to figure out meaning from the context.

Write the word or phrase that best completes the statement or answers the question.

1. The third Abbasid caliph, _____, attempted unsuccessfully to reconcile moderate Shi'a to the Abbasid dynasty.

2. The _____ Turks were nomadic invaders from central Asia who ruled in the name of the Abbasid caliphs from the mid-11th century.

3. The Muslim commander who reconquered territory from Christian rulers in Palestine was _____.

4. The _____ were Islamic mystics who were largely responsible for the conversion of southeast Asia.

5. The Arab general who conquered Sind and added it to the Umayyad Empire was _____.

6. The Indian system of mathematical notation was known as _____ and was used in two scientific revolutions.

7. The Turkic dynasty established in Afghanistan in 962, the _____, was responsible for the invasion of the Indian subcontinent.

8. The ruler who established an independent Muslim kingdom with its capital at Delhi was _____.

9. _____ was a Buddhist trading empire that controlled trade through the Malacca Strait between Malaya and Sumatra.

10. Islam was disseminated to other ports from the most powerful trading state on North Java, _____.

Choose the one alternative that best completes the statement or answers the question.

1. Which of the following was *NOT* a reason for the decline of the Abbasid Empire?
a. the collapse of the cities
b. continued Shi'a resistance to Abbasid rule
c. indulgent overspending by Abbasid rulers
d. the difficulty of solving the problem dynastic succession

2. How did the Shi'is react to the later Abbasid dynasty?
a. They accepted them as the rightful rulers and became the strongest supporters of the Abbasid caliphs.
b. Various Shi'i groups participated in peasant uprisings.
c. They forced the Abbasids to abdicate in favor of a family more closely related to the Prophet.
d. Shi'i sects were eliminated by the Abbasids.

3. Which of the following groups did not capture Baghdad?
a. Mongols
b. Seljuk Turks
c. Buyids
d. Crusaders

4. Which of the following statements concerning the Crusades is most accurate?
a. The Crusaders were successful only because of the political fragmentation of Islam and the element of surprise.
b. Crusader strongholds in the Holy Land were held by the West until the 18th century.
c. The Crusaders succeeded because of the overwhelming superiority of Western military technology.
d. Jewish support for the Christian Crusaders guaranteed their victory in the Holy Land.

5. What was the trend in urbanization during the Abbasid period?
a. Because the Abbasids abandoned Baghdad for other capitals, cities tended to wither and die.
b. Successive invasions led to a decline in urbanization.
c. Despite a decline in the agricultural economy, towns continued to grow rapidly.
d. Towns established in the early years of the dynasty were able to hold their own, but there was little growth.

6. Which of the following was a literary figure during the Abbasid period?
a. Muhammad ibn Qasim
b. al-Ghazali
c. Omar Khayyam
d. Mahmud of Ghazni

7. What region of India did the Muslims first conquer under Muhammad ibn Qasim?
a. Nepal
b. Sind
c. Delhi
d. Rajputana

8. Which of the following statements concerning the Delhi sultanate is most accurate?
a. Delhi sultans descended from Arabs who first entered India in Sind.
b. The Delhi sultanate was unique in that it possessed little military power.
c. Support of their armies and the maintenance of a sumptuous court were the primary objectives of the Delhi sultans.
d. The Delhi sultanate was able to break Muslim dependence on local Hindu ruling elites.

9. Bhaktic cults stressed
a. strict monotheism.
b. the importance of a strong emotional bond between the devotee and the god or goddess.
c. a conservative interpretation of Islamic religious texts.
d. the restriction of religious activities to upper caste groups.

10. What city proved to be the key to the conversion of mainland Southeast Asia?
a. Malacca
b. Shrivijaya
c. Demak
d. Bombay

READING REVIEW: MAKING CONNECTIONS

After reading and studying the chapter, review your understanding by answering each of the following questions, which emphasize important ideas within the chapter.

1. What were the causes of the weaknesses of the later Abbasid Empire?

2. What was the economy of the later Abbasid Empire?

3. What were the stages of Islamic incursion into India?

4. To what extent were the Muslims successful in converting the peoples of Southeast Asia to Islam?

5. How were Muslims affected by Indian culture?

6. How did Islam spread to southeast Asia?

CHAPTER 8
African Civilizations and the Spread of Islam

Complete the following exercises in order *as you read* the chapter.

INTRODUCTION

Chapter introductions are a valuable guide to the material you are about to read, telling you what topics will be covered and how they fit together. If you keep the "big picture" provided by the introduction in mind as you read the chapter, you will find it much easier to organize your notes, identify important information, and avoid getting lost in the details. With this in mind, re-read the introduction to Chapter 8. As you read, make a list of the key topics you expect to learn about.

Key Topics

_____

_____

_____

_____

_____

_____

_____

_____

_____

_____

_____

_____

_____

_____

_____

_____

_____

_____

_____

_____

1. AFRICAN SOCIETIES: DIVERSITY AND SIMILARITIES

As you read this section in your textbook, complete the outline below with the main ideas about diversity and similarities within African societies.

I. African Societies: Diversity and Similarities

  A. Societies With and Without States

    1.

    2.

    3.

  B. Common Elements in African Societies

    1.

    2.

    3.

    4.

    5.

  C. The Arrival of Islam in North Africa

    1.

    2.

    3.

    4.

    5.

  D. The Christian Kingdoms: Nubia and Ethiopia

    1.

    2.

    3.

2. AFRICAN SOCIETIES: DIVERSITY AND SIMILARITIES

As you read this section in your textbook, complete the outline below with the main ideas Islam in Africa.

FOCUS QUESTION: *How did Islam enter Africa?*

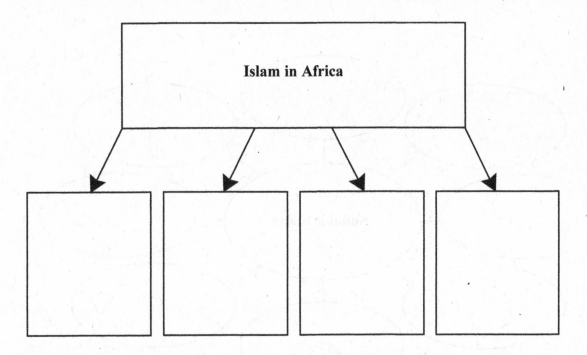

Using the information in your chart, write a brief answer to the Focus Question.

3. KINGDOMS OF THE GRASSLANDS

As you read this section in your textbook, complete the chart below with the main ideas about the Sudanic states.

FOCUS QUESTION: *What were the Sudanic states and how were they organized?*

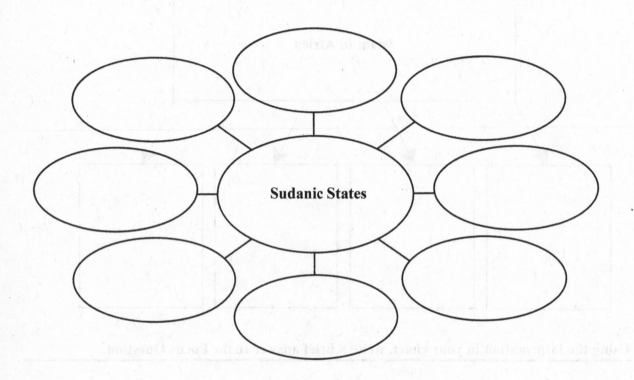

Using the information in your concept web, write a brief answer to the Focus Question.

4. KINGDOMS OF THE GRASSLANDS

As you read this section in your textbook, complete the chart below to summarize the main ideas about Sundiata's expansion of the Mali Empire.

FOCUS QUESTION: *How did the emperor Sundiata create theMali Empire?*

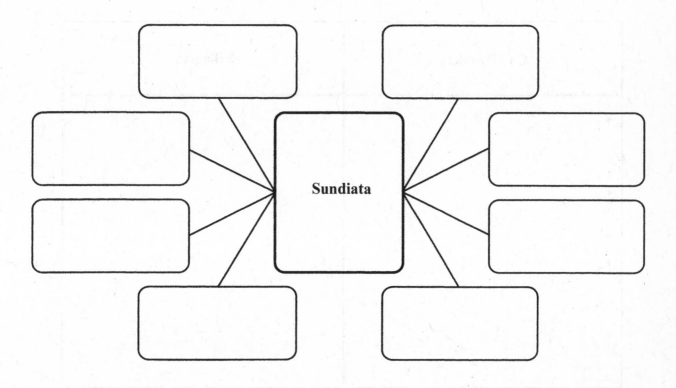

Using the information in your chart, write a brief answer to the Focus Question.

5. KINGDOMS OF THE GRASSLANDS

As you read this section in your textbook, complete the chart below to compare and contrast cities and villages in Mali and other Sudanic states.

City Dwellers	Villagers
•	•
•	•
•	•
•	•

6. KINGDOMS OF THE GRASSLANDS

As you read this section in your textbook, complete the chart below with the main ideas about political and social life in the Sudanic states.

Political Life	Social Life
• _____	• _____
_____	_____
_____	_____
_____	_____
• _____	• _____
_____	_____
_____	_____
_____	_____
• _____	• _____
_____	_____
_____	_____
_____	_____
• _____	• _____
_____	_____
_____	_____

7. THE SWAHILI COAST OF EAST AFRICA

As you read this section in your textbook, complete the chart outline below with the main ideas about the Swahili coast of East Africa.

FOCUS QUESTION: *What influence did religion and trade have on the development of East Africa?*

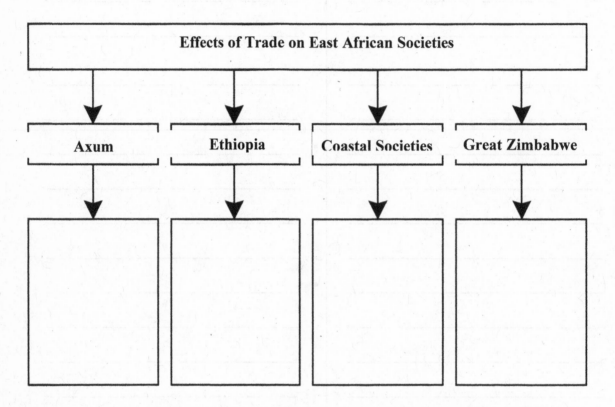

Using the information in your chart, write a brief answer to the Focus Question.

8. PEOPLES OF THE FOREST AND PLAINS

As you read this section in your textbook, complete the chart below to summarize the main ideas characteristics about societies in the interior and forests of West Africa.

Yoruba	•
	•
	•
	•
	•
Benin	•
	•
	•
Central African Kingdoms	•
	•
	•
Kongo	•
	•
	•
Mwene Mutapa	•
	•
	•
	•
	•

TERMS, EVENTS, PEOPLE

The following terms, people, and events are important to your understanding of the chapter. Define each one.

Stateless societies

Almoravids

Almohadis

Sahel

Sudanic states

Mali

Juula

Sundiata

Axum

Timbuktu

Songhay

Askia Muhammad

Hausa states

Demographic transition

Nok

Yoruba

Ile-Ife

Benin

Kongo Kingdom

Great Zimbabwe

MY KEY TERMS

Write down terms that are unfamiliar. How are the words used? Do other words or examples reveal their meaning? Try to figure out meaning from the context.

Write the word or phrase that best completes the statement or answers the question.

1. African societies organized around kinship or other forms of obligation and lacking the concentration of political power were _____ societies.

2. Malinke merchants, _____, formed small partnerships to carry out trade throughout the Mali Empire.

3. Two of the most significant "port" cities of Mali were Jenne and _____, which lay just off the flood plain on the great bend in the Niger River.

4. The successor state to Mali was the independent kingdom of _____, which formed under a Berber dynasty.

5. The string of urbanized trading ports including Mogadishu, Mombassa, Malindi, Kilwa, Pate, and Zanzibar shared the common Bantu-based and Arabic-influenced _____ language.

6. The Arabic traveler and commentator _____ described African societies and cultures in his travel accounts.

7. The change from slow to rapid population growth often associated with the process of industrialization is referred to as the _____.

8. The _____ culture featured a highly developed art style that flourished between 500 B.C.E. and 200 C.E.

9. The _____ city-states developed in northern Nigeria circa 1200 C.E.

10. By the late 15th century, the Kingdom of _____ on the lower Congo River was flourishing around its capital at Mbanza Kongo.

Choose the one alternative that best completes the statement or answers the question.

1. Which of the following was *NOT* a reason for the decline of the Abbasid Empire?
a. the collapse of the cities
b. continued Shi'a resistance to Abbasid rule
c. indulgent overspending by Abbasid rulers
d. the difficulty of solving the problem dynastic succession

2. How did the Shi'is react to the later Abbasid dynasty?
a. They accepted them as the rightful rulers and became the strongest supporters of the Abbasid caliphs.
b. Various Shi'i groups participated in peasant uprisings.
c. They forced the Abbasids to abdicate in favor of a family more closely related to the Prophet.
d. Shi'i sects were eliminated by the Abbasids.

3. Which of the following groups did not capture Baghdad?
a. Mongols
b. Seljuk Turks
c. Buyids
d. Crusaders

4. Which of the following statements concerning the Crusades is most accurate?
a. The Crusaders were successful only because of the political fragmentation of Islam and the element of surprise.
b. Crusader strongholds in the Holy Land were held by the West until the 18th century.
c. The Crusaders succeeded because of the overwhelming superiority of Western military technology.
d. Jewish support for the Christian Crusaders guaranteed their victory in the Holy Land.

5. What was the trend in urbanization during the Abbasid period?
a. Because the Abbasids abandoned Baghdad for other capitals, cities tended to wither and die.
b. Successive invasions led to a decline in urbanization.
c. Despite a decline in the agricultural economy, towns continued to grow rapidly.
d. Towns established in the early years of the dynasty were able to hold their own, but there was little growth.

6. Which of the following was a literary figure during the Abbasid period?
a. Muhammad ibn Qasim
b. al-Ghazali
c. Omar Khayyam
d. Mahmud of Ghazni

7. What region of India did the Muslims first conquer under Muhammad ibn Qasim?
a. Nepal
b. Sind
c. Delhi
d. Rajputana

8. Which of the following statements concerning the Delhi sultanate is most accurate?
a. Delhi sultans descended from Arabs who first entered India in Sind.
b. The Delhi sultanate was unique in that it possessed little military power.
c. Support of their armies and the maintenance of a sumptuous court were the primary objectives of the Delhi sultans.
d. The Delhi sultanate was able to break Muslim dependence on local Hindu ruling elites.

9. Bhaktic cults stressed
a. strict monotheism.
b. the importance of a strong emotional bond between the devotee and the god or goddess.
c. a conservative interpretation of Islamic religious texts.
d. the restriction of religious activities to upper caste groups.

10. What city proved to be the key to the conversion of mainland Southeast Asia?
a. Malacca
b. Shrivijaya
c. Demak
d. Bombay

After reading and studying the chapter, review your understanding by answering each of the following questions, which emphasize important ideas within the chapter.

1. What were the common elements of African society prior to the incursion of Islam?

2. What were the Sudanic states and how were they organized?

3. How did Islam fuse with indigenous customs within the Sudanic states?

4. What was the connection between East Africa and Islam?

5. Where did cultures develop in Africa that were *NOT* affected by Islam? What was the nature of their organization?

CHAPTER 9
Civilization in Eastern Europe: Byzantium and Orthodox Europe

Complete the following exercises in order *as you read* the chapter.

INTRODUCTION

Chapter introductions are a valuable guide to the material you are about to read, telling you what topics will be covered and how they fit together. If you keep the "big picture" provided by the introduction in mind as you read the chapter, you will find it much easier to organize your notes, identify important information, and avoid getting lost in the details. With this in mind, re-read the introduction to Chapter 9. As you read, make a list of the key topics you expect to learn about.

Key Topics

_____

_____

_____

_____

_____

_____

_____

_____

_____

_____

_____

_____

_____

_____

_____

_____

_____

1. CIVILIZATION IN EASTERN EUROPE

As you read this section in your textbook, complete the outline below with the main ideas about the significance of the Byzantine Empire.

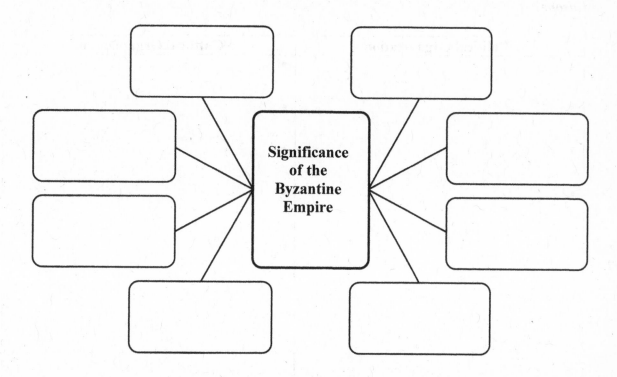

2. THE BYZANTINE EMPIRE

As you read this section in your textbook, take notes on the political and cultural organization of the Byzantine Empire.

FOCUS QUESTION: *How did the Byzantine Empire affect the development of eastern Europe?*

Political Organization	Cultural Organization
•	•
•	•
•	•
•	•

Using the information in your chart, write a brief answer to the Focus Question.

3. THE SPLIT BETWEEN EASTERN AND WESTERN CHRISTIANITY

As you read this section in your textbook, complete the outline below with the main ideas about the divisions the two main branches of Christianity.

I. Eastern and Western Christianity

    A.

       1.

       2.

       3.

       4.

    B.

       1.

       2.

       3.

       4.

       5.

4. THE SPLIT BETWEEN EASTERN AND WESTERN CHRISTIANITY

As you read this section in your textbook, complete the chart below to summarize the main ideas about the decline of the Byzantine Empire.

FOCUS QUESTION: *What made the Byzantine empire rich and successful for so long, and why did it finally crumble?*

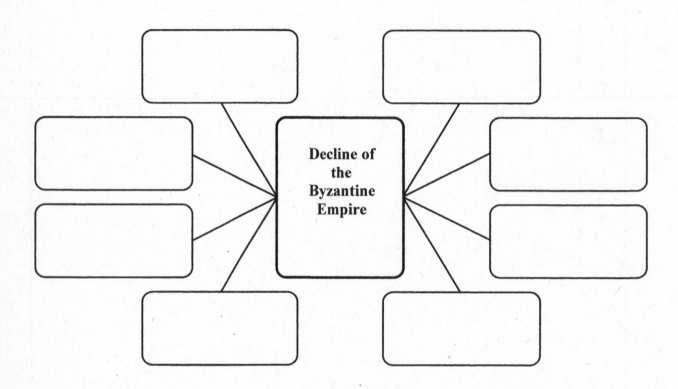

Using the information in your chart, write a brief answer to the Focus Question.

5. THE SPREAD OF CIVILIZATION IN EASTERN EUROPE

As you read this section in your textbook, complete the concept web below to summarize the rise of Eastern European civilization.

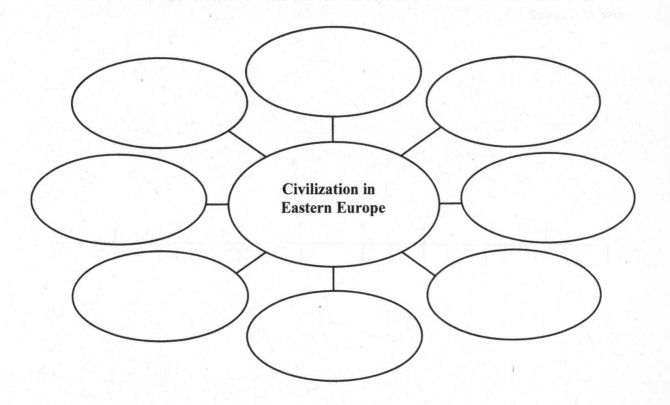

6. THE EMERGENCE OF KIEVAN RUS'

As you read this section in your textbook, complete the timeline events to sequence the events in the rise of Russia from 700s to the 1500s.

FOCUS QUESTION: *How did geography and the migration of different peoples influence the rise of Russia?*

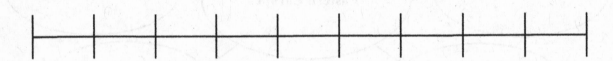

Using the information in your chart, write a brief answer to the Focus Question.

TERMS, EVENTS, PEOPLE

The following terms, people, and events are important to your understanding of the chapter. Define each one.

Byzantine Empire

Balkans

Justinian

Theodora

Belisarius

Greek fire

Bulgaria

icons

iconoclasm

Cyril and Methodius

Rurik

Vladimir I

Russian Orthodoxy

Yaroslav I

boyars

Tatars

Constantinople

Huns.

Sassanian Empire

Procopius

Hellenistic culture

Tsar

Cyrillic alphabet

Rurik

MY KEY TERMS

Write down terms that are unfamiliar. How are the words used? Do other words or examples reveal their meaning? Try to figure out meaning from the context.

Write the word or phrase that best completes the statement or answers the question.

1. The eastern half of the Roman Empire survived after the 5th century as the _____.

2. The Byzantine emperor _____ was responsible for the attempted reconstruction of the political unity of the ancient Roman Empire.

3. One of the military technological achievements of the Byzantine Empire was the invention of _____, a weapon used against the Arab fleets.

4. The Slavic kingdom established in the northern portions of the Balkan peninsula that presented a major challenge to the Byzantine Empire was _____.

5. Images of religious figures that became objects of veneration in Byzantine Christianity were _____.

6. In 1204, a crusade led by _____ merchants conquered Byzantium and temporarily unseated the Byzantine emperor.

7. The form of Christianity that developed in Byzantium and spread to Russia and the Balkans was referred to as _____ Christianity.

8. The Russian ruler credited with converting the country to Christianity was _____.

9. Russian aristocrats or _____ had less political power than their counterparts in western Europe.

10. In 1236, a large force of Mongols, called by the Russians _____, captured the major Russian cities.

MULTIPLE CHOICE REVIEW

Choose the one alternative that best completes the statement or answers the question.

1. The significance of the Byzantine Empire included all of the following *EXCEPT*
a. the empire's ability to survive for almost 1,000 years.
b. the importance of the empire's capital as a major urban center.
c. the ability of the empire to spread its cultural and political influence to the Balkans and southern Russia.
d. the empire's conquest of the Ottoman Empire and its inclusion of all of the Middle East.

2. Which of the following represents a similarity between the spread of civilization in eastern and western Europe?
a. The political and theological organization of Christianity was identical.
b. Commercial patterns in both cases ran east-west.
c. More northerly political units in both halves of Europe struggled for political definition.
d. Western and eastern Europe enjoyed similar levels of political sophistication and organization during most of the postclassical period.

3. The capital of the Byzantine Empire and its commercial center was located at
a. Rome.
b. Nicaea.
c. Constantinople.
d. Baghdad.

4. The great church built by Justinian was
a. St. Peter's.
b. The Cathedral of St. Dimitry.
c. Sts. Cyril and Methodius.
d. Hagia Sophia.

5. Which of the following was a result of the conflict between the Byzantine Empire and the Arab Muslims?
a. The Islamic threat to the Byzantine Empire was permanently removed.
b. The position of the small farmers in the empire was weakened as a result of heavy taxation.
c. The Byzantine Empire was able to recover Syria, Palestine, and Egypt.
d. The commercial dominance of Constantinople was destroyed during the 8th century.

6. The military force of the Byzantine Empire
a. was recruited from 'barbarians' outside the empire's frontiers.
b. was a paid, professional army located in Constantinople.
c. was recruited from the peasants of the empire in return for grants of heritable land.
d. was impermanent, only recruited for the few military crises of the empire.

7. Images of religious objects venerated as part of the religious practices of the Orthodox Church were
a. icons.
b. idols.
c. filioque.
d. adiaphora.

8. Cyril and Methodius were responsible for what accomplishment?
a. the solution to the iconoclastic controversy
b. the creation of a written script for the Slavic language
c. the conversion of Poland to Orthodox Christianity
d. the conversion of what is now the Czech Republic to Roman Catholicism

9. Which characteristic of Byzantine society was *NOT* adopted by Kievan Rus'?
a. ornate churches filled with icons
b. the practice of monogamy
c. an elaborate education system
d. a monastic movement stressing prayer and charity

10. How did the Tartar (Mongol) conquest of Russia shape Russian history?
a. It destroyed Christianity in Russia.
b. It further separated it from the cultures in western Europe.
c. It led to the destruction of the Russian nobility.
d. It sparked a flourishing in Russian literature.

READING REVIEW: MAKING CONNECTIONS

After reading and studying the chapter, review your understanding by answering each of the following questions, which emphasize important ideas within the chapter.

1. What was the significance of the Byzantine Empire to the civilization of Europe?

2. What were the factors in the decline of the Byzantine Empire?

3. How did the Byzantine Empire influence Russia?

4. How did eastern Europe fall behind western Europe in terms of political development?

5. In what ways was the culture of Kievan Russia an extension of the Byzantine Empire?

CHAPTER 10
A New Civilization Emerges in Western Europe

Complete the following exercises in order *as you read* the chapter.

INTRODUCTION

Chapter introductions are a valuable guide to the material you are about to read, telling you what topics will be covered and how they fit together. If you keep the "big picture" provided by the introduction in mind as you read the chapter, you will find it much easier to organize your notes, identify important information, and avoid getting lost in the details. With this in mind, re-read the introduction to Chapter 10. As you read, make a list of the key topics you expect to learn about.

Key Topics

_____

_____

_____

_____

_____

_____

_____

_____

_____

_____

_____

_____

_____

_____

_____

_____

_____

_____

1. STAGES OF POSTCLASSICAL DEVELOPMENT

As you read this section in your textbook, use the table below to identify the main ideas for each of the topics in the section.

Stages of Postclassical Development	
The Manorial System	
The Church: Political and Spiritual Power	
Charlemagne and His Successors	
New Economic and Urban Vigor	
Feudal Monarchies and Political Advances	
Limited Government	
The West's Expansionist Impulse	
Religious Reform and Evolution	
The High Middle Ages	

2. STAGES OF POSTCLASSICAL DEVELOPMENT

As you read this section in your textbook, use the table below to identify main ideas about manorial system and feudalism.

FOCUS QUESTION: *How did manorial system and feudalism emerge and shape medieval life?*

Manorial System	Feudalism

Using the information in your, write a brief answer to the Focus Question.

3. STAGES OF POSTCLASSICAL DEVELOPMENT

As you read this section in your textbook, use the concept web below to identify the main ideas about the political and spiritual power of the Church.

FOCUS QUESTION: *How did the Church play a vital role in medieval life?*

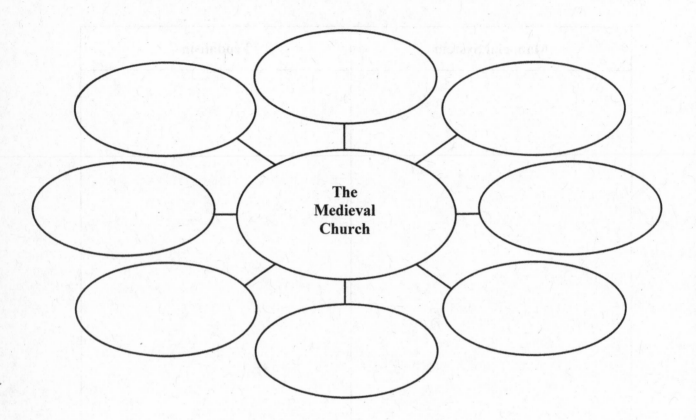

Using the information from your concept web, write a brief answer to the Focus Question.

4. STAGES OF POSTCLASSICAL DEVELOPMENT

As you read this section in your textbook, complete the concept web below to identify the causes of the Crusades in the top ovals and the effects of the Crusades in the lower ovals.

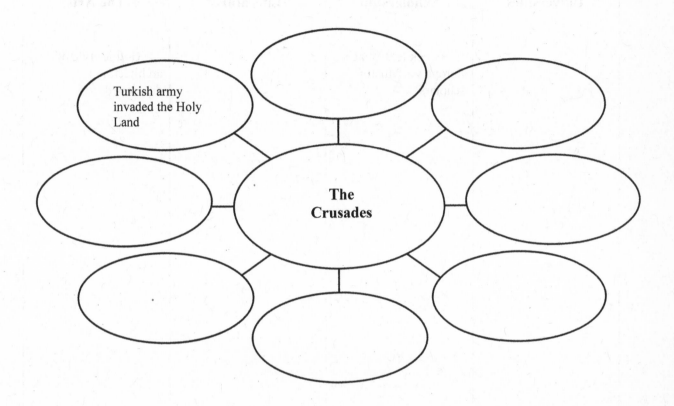

Turkish army invaded the Holy Land

The Crusades

5. WESTERN CULTURE IN THE POSTCLASSICAL ERA

As you read this section in your textbook, complete the flowchart below to identify the cultural and intellectual flowering of the Middle Ages.

Universities	Scholarship	Literature	The Arts
	Greek texts reach Europe via Muslim scholars		Gothic style of architecture is developed

6. CHANGING ECONOMIC AND SOCIAL FORMS IN THE POSTCLASSICAL CENTURIES

As you read this section in your textbook, use the table below to identify the main ideas for each of the topics in the section.

New Strains in Rural Life	
Growth of Trade and Banking	
Limited Sphere for Women	

7. THE DECLINE OF THE MEDIEVAL SYNTHESIS

As you read this section of your textbook, complete the chart below to identify the causes of the decline of the medieval society.

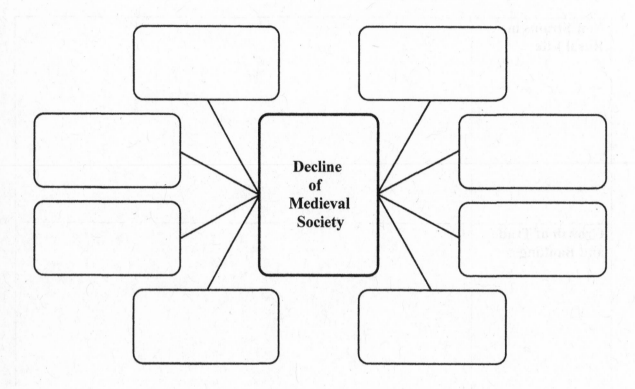

TERMS, EVENTS, PEOPLE

The following terms, people, and events are important to your understanding of the chapter. Define each one.

Middle Ages

Gothic

Vikings

Manorialism

Three-field system

Clovis

Carolingians

Charlemagne

Holy Roman emperors

Feudalism

Vassals

William the Conqueror

Magna Carta

Hundred Years War

Pope Urban II

Investiture

St. Clare of Assisi

Gregory VII

Peter Abelard

Thomas Aquinas

Scholasticism

Troubadours

Hanseatic League

Guilds

Black Death

MY KEY TERMS

Write down terms that are unfamiliar. How are the words used? Do other words or examples reveal their meaning? Try to figure out meaning from the context.

SHORT ANSWER REVIEW

Write the word or phrase that best completes the statement or answers the question.

1. An architectural style developed during the Middle Ages in western Europe, _____ architecture featured pointed arches and flying buttresses.

2. _____ was the system that described economic and political relations between landlords and their peasant laborers.

3. _____ described relationships among military elites in which greater lords provided protection and aid to lesser lords.

4. The _____ were the royal house of the Franks from the 8th to the 10th century.

5. The Frankish monarch _____ was responsible for defeating the Muslims of Spain in the Battle of Tours in 732.

6. The system of agricultural cultivation by the 9th century in much of western Europe was the _____ system, utilizing one-third fallow, one-third spring grains, and one-third winter grains.

7. _____ invaded England from Normandy in 1066 and implemented a feudal system in England.

8. The _____ between England and France was fought between 1337 and 1453 to establish the emerging claims of national states.

9. An organization of cities in northern Germany for the purpose of establishing a commercial alliance was called the _____.

10. Sworn associations of people in the same business or trade in a single city, _____, stressed security and guaranteed good workmanship.

Choose the one alternative that best completes the statement or answers the question.

1. In which of the following ways was the medieval West *NOT* like other civilizations?
a. The medieval period saw the spread of civilization outside the Mediterranean zone core to new areas in northern Europe.
b. New religious beliefs accompanied the spread of civilization.
c. The medieval West remained culturally backward, compared to other civilizations.
d. Western Europe participated in the emerging international community.

2. Following the fall of Rome, where was the center of the postclassical West?
a. in the former Roman colonies of Spain and Portugal
b. in Italy, particularly Rome
c. in France, England, Germany, and the Low Countries,
d. Greece and the Balkan region

3. Manorialism was the system that
a. described economic and political relations between landlords and their peasant laborers.
b. secular authorities used to name bishops.
c. defined relationships between members of the military elite.
d. united the traditions of classical rationalism with medieval Christianity.

4. Which of the following statements concerning the early medieval manorial system is *NOT* true?
a. It was technologically sophisticated.
b. It had originated in the Roman Empire.
c. Its obligations bore heavily on the serfs.
d. Agricultural productivity was low.

5. What Frankish monarch was able to establish a substantial empire after 800?
a. Clovis
b. Charles Martel
c. Pepin III
d. Charlemagne

6. Where was the greatest concentration of urbanization after the 10th century?
a. Italy and the Low Countries
b. England and France
c. France and the Holy Roman Empire
d. England and Scandinavia

7. Which of the following was a result of the Crusades?
a. Western knights carved out a kingdom in the Holy Land that lasted until the 15th century.
b. The Fourth Crusade aided in the defense of Constantinople and preserved the integrity of the Byzantine Empire.
c. The Crusades demonstrated a new Western superiority in the wider world.
d. The Crusades helped to open the West to new cultural and economic influences from the East.

8. Vassals were
a. grants of land given to lesser members of the military elite in return for military service.
b. agricultural laborers in the manorial system.
c. members of the military elite who received land in return for service.
d. greater lords within the military elite who commanded military bands.

9. How did the intellectual endeavors of medieval scholars differ before and after 1000?
a. Before 1000, scholars were limited to copying ancient texts, but after 1000 a greater synthesis of rationalism and theology was achieved.
b. After 1000, they abandoned classical rationalism completely in favor of more mystical goals.
c. Prior to 1000, more innovative classical techniques were utilized, but after 1000 the growing authority of the Church limited the use of classical authors.
d. After 1000, classical rationalism eliminated more mystical approaches to Christian theology.

10. Which of the following was not a result of the Hundred Years' War?
a. Kings reduced their reliance on feudal forces in favor of paid armies.
b. An English victory.
c. Foot soldiers began to achieve parity or even an advantage over mounted knights.
d. Devastation and antifeudal innovations.

After reading and studying the chapter, review your understanding by answering each of the following questions, which emphasize important ideas within the chapter.

1. What defines the postclassical period in western Europe?

2. What were the signs of vitality in western Europe?

3. What developments in the 9th and 10th centuries pointed the way to political and economic recovery?

4. What were the signs of economic prosperity after 1000?

CHAPTER 11
The Americas on the Eve of Invasion

Complete the following exercises in order *as you read* the chapter.

INTRODUCTION

Introductions provide a valuable guide to the material you are about to read, telling you what topics will be covered and how they fit together. If you keep the "big picture" provided by the introduction in mind as you read the chapter, You will find it much easier to organize your notes, identify important information, and avoid getting lost in the details. With this in mind, re-read the introduction to Chapter 11. As you read, make a list of the key topics you expect to learn about.

Key Topics

_____

_____

_____

_____

_____

_____

_____

_____

_____

_____

_____

_____

_____

_____

_____

_____

_____

_____

_____

_____

_____

1. POSTCLASSIC MESOAMERICA, 1000-1500 C.E.

As you read this section in your textbook, use the table included below to take notes on the key characteristics of Aztec civilization.

Politics	Society and Religion	Economics
•	• Stratified society under supreme ruler	•

2. POSTCLASSIC MESOAMERICA, 1000-1500 C.E.

As you read this section in your textbook, complete the table included below to summarize the key characteristics of Toltec and Aztec civilizations.

FOCUS QUESTION: *How did the Toltecs and Aztecs rise to power?*

Toltecs	Aztecs
•	•
•	•
•	•
•	•

Using the information in your chart, write a brief answer to the Focus Question.

3. AZTEC SOCIETY IN TRANSITION

As you read this section in your textbook, complete the following outline to identify major trends in mature Aztec society and describe their causes and consequences.

I. A Widening Social Gulf

  A. The Role of Caplulli in Aztec Life

    1.

    2.

    3.

    4.

  B.

    1.

    2.

  C.

  D.

II. Overcoming Technological Constraints

  A.

    1.

    2.

  B.

    1.

    2.

III. A Tribute Empire

  A.

 B.

    1.

    2.

4. TWANTINSUYU: WORLD OF THE INCAS

As you read this section of your textbook, use the table included below to take notes on the components of Inca imperial government.

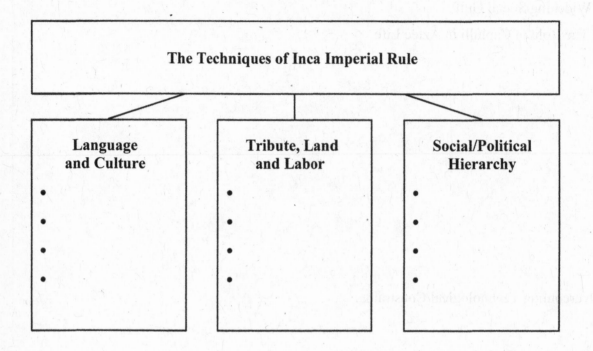

5. THE OTHER PEOPLES OF THE AMERICAS

As you read this section in your textbook, complete the following outline to describe the general characteristics of the peoples of the Americas.

I. How Many Peoples?

  A. Population estimates and the historical record

    1.

    2.

  B. Differing Cultural Patterns

    1.

    2.

    3.

    4.

    5.

    6.

    7.

  C. American Diversity in World Context

    1.

    2.

    3.

6. THE OTHER PEOPLES OF THE AMERICAS

As you read this section of your textbook, complete the concept web below to summarize the main aspects of Native American diversity in North America by 1500.

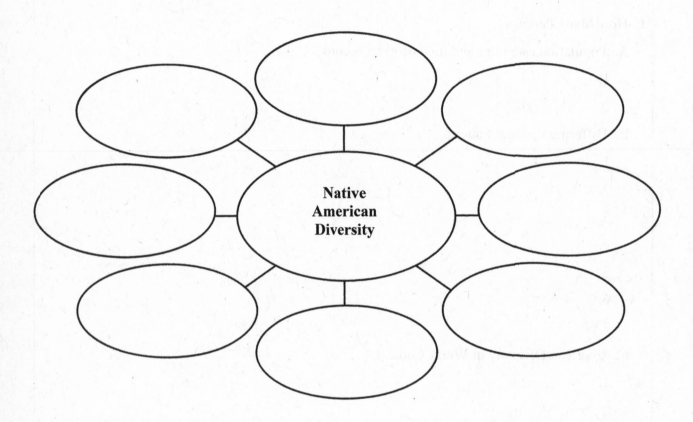

TERMS, PEOPLE, EVENTS

The following terms, people, and events are important to your understanding of the chapter. Write a brief definition of each.

Indian

Toltecs

Aztecs

Tenochtitlan

Pipiltin

Tlacaelel

Huitzilopochtli

Calpulli

Chinampas.

Pochteca

Inca socialism

Twantinsuyu

Inca

Pachacuti.

Topac Yupanqui

Huayna Capac

Split inheritance

Temple of the Sun

Curacas

Tambos

Mita

Quipu

Hernan Cortés

Anasazi

Hopewell

Pochteca

"Flowery death"

Tihuanaco and Huari

Metates

Viracucha

Huacas

Yanas

MY KEY TERMS

Write down terms that are unfamiliar. How are the words used? Do other words or examples reveal their meaning? Try to figure out meaning from the context.

Write the word or phrase that best completes the statement or answers the question.

1. The term _____ was a misnomer created by Columbus for Native Americans when he thought he had reached the Indies.

2. The Mexica or _____ penetrated into the sedentary agricultural zone of Mexico after Toltec collapse and established an empire circa 1325.

3. Founded circa 1325 on a marshy island in Lake Texcoco, _____ became the center of Aztec power.

4. _____, or death while taking prisoners for sacrifice, was thought by the Aztecs to be a fitting end to a noble life and an assurance of eternity in the highest heaven.

5. The modern interpretation of Aztec society created by Marvin Harris, the _____.

6. The group of clans centered at Cuzco that was able to create an empire in Andean civilization circa 1438 was the _____.

7. The Inca practice of descent, _____, granted all titles and political power to the ruler's successor, but wealth and land remained in the hands of male descendants for support of the cult of the dead Inca's mummy.

8. It is estimated that in 1492, the total human population of the western hemisphere was approximately _____ million.

9. The _____ were a class of people removed from their ayllus to serve permanently as servants, artisans, or workers for the Inca and his family.

10. The system of knotted strings utilized by the Incas in place of a writing system, _____ could contain numerical and other types of information for censuses and financial records.

MULTIPLE CHOICE REVIEW

Choose the one alternative that best completes the statement or answers the question.

1. During the postclassical period, societies in the Americas
a. lacked a sense of common identity that bound them all together.
b. did not develop large urban centers.
c. failed to develop imperial forms of government.
d. were united under a single government.

2. After the sack of Tula in the 10th century, the center of population and political power in Mesoamerica moved to
a. Yucatan.
b. the valley of Mexico and the shores of a chain of lakes in that basin.
c. Teotihuacan.
d. Chimor.

3. What was the impact of expansion and conquest on the Aztec social system?
a. From a loose association of clans, Aztec society became more hierarchical.
b. Conquest opened up Aztec society to incursions by the indigenous peoples, who began to form a trained bureaucracy.
c. Aztec society was transformed in the sense that the Mexica adopted the social patterns of the Maya.
d. Despite the stress of war and invasion, the Aztec society remained remarkably egalitarian.

4. What was the significance of the god Huitzilopochtli?
a. He was the god of rain, adapted by the Aztecs from earlier Mesoamerican deities.
b. He was the creator deity of the Aztecs, associated with the moon.
c. He was the single god of salvation proposed by a religious reformer but rejected by the Aztecs.
d. He was the patron god of the Aztecs most closely associated with the cult of warfare and sacrifice.

5. What was the nature of the Aztec administration of subject territories?
a. The Aztecs placed members of the royal family as rulers over subject peoples.
b. All territories became part of a centralized administration run by a trained bureaucracy.
c. Conquered territories were often left relatively unchanged under their old rulers as long as they recognized Aztec supremacy and paid tribute.
d. The Aztecs established a military administration with subject territories controlled by regional generals.

6. Following the decline of the horizon states of Tihuanaco and Huari,
a. a number of large states such as Chimor continued to be important.
b. a general breakdown of power similar to the situation in central Mexico after the decline of Teotihuacan occurred.
c. an invasion of nomadic peoples from the northern frontiers of the Andean region established small city-states.
d. the Incas immediately established their empire.

7. What was the Inca practice of split inheritance?
a. The throne passed to two descendants from the previous ruler's family.
b. The ruler's wealth was equally divided among all male heirs.
c. The inheritance passed through the family of the senior wife to her oldest brother.
d. All political power and titles went to the ruler's successor, but his wealth was kept in the hands of the male descendants to support the cult of the dead ruler's mummy.

8. Which statement best characterizes the relationship between the Inca and local ethnic leaders?
a. The Inca routinely sacrificed captured local leaders to their gods.
b. Incan control over local leaders was weak, and rebellions were common.
c. Local leaders considered the equivalent of Incan nobility.
d. Local leaders were left in place but were subordinate to Incan administrators.

9. Which of the following practices was common to the Aztec and the Inca empires?
a. the extensive use of colonization
b. a tribute system
c. a merchant class
d. a writing system

10. Which of the following statements concerning the population of the Americas is most true?
a. The population of the Americas before 1500 is easily calculated.
b. North America was more densely populated than Mesoamerica and the Andes.
c. The population of the Americas was probably close to contemporary Europe's, excluding Russia.
d. The early 20th-century estimate of 8.4 million still seems the most accurate.

READING CHECK: MAKING CONNECTIONS

After reading and studying the chapter, review your understanding by answering each of the following questions, which emphasize important ideas within the chapter.

1. What was the relationship of the Aztecs to the Toltecs?

2. What was the political and economic organization of the Aztec empire?

3. What was the social organization of the Aztec empire? How did it change over time?

4. What was the political and economic organization of the Inca empire?

5. What was the social organization of the Inca empire?

6. How did the other Indian groups of the Americas differ from the imperial cultures?

CHAPTER 12
Reunification and Renaissance in Chinese Civilization: The Era of the Tang and Song Dynasties

Complete the following exercises in order *as you read* the chapter.

INTRODUCTION

Introductions provide a valuable guide to the material you are about to read, telling you what topics will be covered and how they fit together. If you keep the "big picture" provided by the introduction in mind as you read the chapter, You will find it much easier to organize your notes, identify important information, and avoid getting lost in the details. With this in mind, re-read the introduction to Chapter 12. As you read, make a list of the key topics you expect to learn about.

Key Topics

_____

_____

_____

_____

_____

_____

_____

_____

_____

_____

_____

_____

_____

_____

_____

_____

_____

1. REBUILDING THE IMPERIAL EDIFICE IN THE SUI-TANG ERA

As you read this section in your textbook, use the table included below to identify the major challenges faced by the Tang government and the policies the Tang devised in response to those challenges.

Chinese Reunification Under the Tang	
Challenges	**Policies**
Rebuilding the Bureaucracy	• Promotion of the scholar-gentry

2. REBUILDING THE IMPERIAL EDIFICE IN THE SUI-TANG ERA

As you read this section in your textbook, complete the outline below to identify the main ideas about state and religion in the Tang and Song Eras.

I. State and Religion in the Tang and Song Eras

    A. Confucianism and Buddhism potential rivals

           1.

           2.

           3.

    B.

           1.

           2.

    C.

           1.

           2.

    D.

           1.

           2.

    E.

3. TANG DECLINE AND THE RISE OF THE SONG

As you read this section of your textbook, create a timeline of the key events in the rise and fall of the Song Dynasty. Use the timeline included below as a starting point.

Rise and Fall of the Song Dynasty	
960	Emergence of Zhao Kuangyin as dominant general in China.
1004	Song begin paying tribute to Khitan.

4. TANG AND SONG PROSPERITY: THE BASIS OF THE GOLDEN AGE:

As you read this section in your textbook, complete the concept web included below to identify important characteristics of the society and economy of China during the Tang and Song eras.

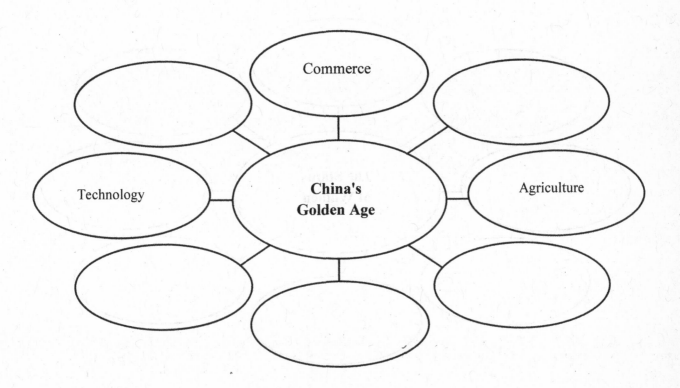

5. TANG AND SONG PROSPERITY: THE BASIS OF THE GOLDEN AGE:

As you read this section in your textbook, complete the concept web included below to identify the main ideas about family and society during the Tang and Song eras.

FOCUS QUESTION: *What was the status of women during the Tang-Song era?*

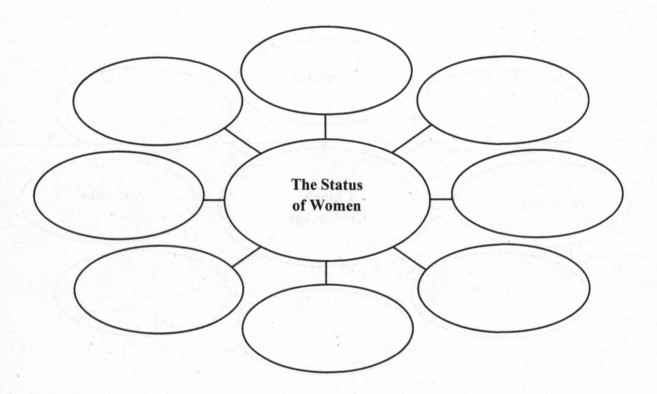

The Status
of Women

Using the information in your concept web, write a brief answer to the Focus Question.

CHAPTER REVIEW

TERMS, PEOPLE, EVENTS

The following terms, people, and events are important to your understanding of the chapter. Write a brief definition of each.

Period of the Five Dynasties

Wendi

Yangd

Li Yuan

Ministry of Public Rites

Jinshi

Chan Buddhism

Mahayana (Pure Land) Buddhism

Wuzong

Yang Guifei

Khitan nomads

Zhao Kuangyin

Zhu Xi

Wang Anshi

Southern Song

Jurchens

Grand Canal

Junks

Changan

Huangzhou.

Foot binding

Bi Sheng

Li Bo

Empress Wu

Xuanzong

Zhao Kuangyin

Liao Dynasty

Sinfication

Neo-Confucians

Tangut tribes

Xi Xia

Jin kingdom

MY KEY TERMS

Write down terms that are unfamiliar. How are the words used? Do other words or examples reveal their meaning? Try to figure out meaning from the context.

Write the word or phrase that best completes the statement or answers the question.

1. _____ was a member of a prominent northern family following the fall of the Han, who proclaimed himself emperor and established the Sui dynasty.

2. Minister for Yangdi, _____, the duke of Tang, took over the empire following the assassination of the last emperor of the Sui dynasty.

3. The _____ variant of Buddhism emphasized the salvationist aspects of the faith and appealed to the masses of Chinese society.

4. A general of nomadic origins named _____ led a widely supported revolt to depose the Tang dynasty in 755.

5. The much-reduced state of the Song dynasty from 1127 to 1279 was referred to as the _____.

6. Chinese ships equipped with watertight bulkheads, stern-post rudders, compasses, and bamboo fenders were called _____.

7. _____ was a Chinese credit instrument that provided vouchers to merchants to be redeemed at the end of the voyage.

8. The Chinese counterpart of the Islamic veil and seclusion, _____, produced pain and restricted women's movement outside the household.

9. The most famous poet of the Tang era, _____, blended images of the mundane world with philosophical musings.

10. The invention of _____ was originally used for entertainment purposes, but by the late Song era was used in military applications as well.

MULTIPLE CHOICE REVIEW

Choose the one alternative that best completes the statement or answers the question.

1. Which of the following was *NOT* characteristic of the period of the Song and Tang dynasties?
a. China was governed by a large, well-educated bureaucracy.
b. Nomadic invaders from the north and west posed little danger.
c. The ruling elites promoted technological innovation.
d. A strong military brought long periods of peace.

2. The collapse of the Sui dynasty was brought on by which of the following?
a. A series of failed wars against Korea and a nearly failed war with Turkic invaders.
b. The advent of European colonization in East Asia.
c. The emperor Yangdi's failure to impose reforms on the bureaucracy.
d. A series of revolts led by Buddhist monks.

3. What made possible the rapid revival of the empire under the Tang?
a. the abandonment of Confucianism in favor of the more widely practiced Buddhism
b. the brevity of the period of political dislocation
c. the willingness of the Tang to abandon traditional approaches to government
d. a revived scholar-gentry elite and a reworked Confucian ideology

4. The support of which of the following groups was most critical to the reunification of China under the Sui?
a. the nomadic warrior elite
b. the ethnic Chinese aristocracy
c. the Buddhist monasteries
d. the Confucian scholar-gentry

5. What was the attitude of the Tang emperors toward the Confucian scholar-gentry?
a. The Tang continued to support the growth of Buddhism at the expense of the scholar gentry.
b. The Tang supported the revival of the scholar-gentry, often at the expense of the aristocracy.
c. The Tang feared the return of the scholar-gentry and continued to support the nomadic aristocracy of China.
d. Confucianism waned during the Tang era and was only resuscitated under the Song.

6. The Ministry of Rites was responsible for the
a. administration of the examination system.
b. regulation of Buddhist monasteries.
c. examination of local administration and trial of poor ministers.
d. coronation of the emperors.

7. Which of the following statements concerning entry into the Chinese bureaucracy is most accurate?
a. Although a higher percentage of candidates received office through the examination system than during the Han dynasty, birth continued to be important.
b. Under the Tang, family connections ceased to be of significance.
c. All officials received positions under the Tang as a result of family position.
d. The examination system was eliminated during the Tang era, and only members of the imperial family served in the bureaucracy.

8. Which of the following statements concerning the Tang dynasty's attitude toward Buddhism is most accurate?
a. Under the Tang, Buddhism became the official religion of the state.
b. Later Tang emperors actually resuscitated Buddhist monasteries, particularly in southern China.
c. Although Empress Wu attempted to have Buddhism recognized as the official religion of the state, later emperors persecuted Buddhists as economic threats to the state.
d. From the outset, Tang rulers persecuted Buddhists.

9. What accounts for the relative weakness of the Song empire?
a. It never succeeded in achieving the degree of centralization that had typified the Tang.
b. The scholar-gentry lost influence under the Song, and the bureaucracy ceased to function.
c. The lack of agricultural productivity produced a general failure of the Chinese economy.
d. The military was subordinated to the scholar-gentry.

10. Which of the following statements concerning the economy in China during the Tang-Song era is *NOT* accurate?
a. The level of urbanization in China increased.
b. The Chinese transportation and communication network deteriorated.
c. The sophistication of Chinese commercial contracts and credit systems increased.
d. The amount of land under cultivation and the yield of Chinese agriculture increased.

158

READING CHECK: MAKING CONNECTIONS

After reading and studying the chapter, review your understanding by answering each of the following questions, which emphasize important ideas within the chapter.

1. How did the Sui dynasty rise to power? What caused its collapse?

2. In what way was the rise of the Tang dynasty associated with the Confucian renaissance?

3. What accounts for the decline of the Tang dynasty?

4. In what way was the Song empire weaker than the Tang?

5. What were the components of economic prosperity during the Tang-Song era?

6. What was the overall impact of the Tang-Song era on Chinese history?

7. What innovations were made during the Tang-Song era?

CHAPTER 13
The Spread of Chinese Civilization: Japan, Korea, and Vietnam

Complete the following exercises in order *as you read* the chapter.

INTRODUCTION

Chapter introductions are a valuable guide to the material you are about to read, telling you what topics will be covered and how they fit together. If you keep the "big picture" provided by the introduction in mind as you read the chapter, you will find it much easier to organize your notes, identify important information, and avoid getting lost in the details. With this in mind, re-read the introduction to Chapter 13. As you read, make a list of the key topics you expect to learn about.

Key Topics

_____

_____

_____

_____

_____

_____

_____

_____

_____

_____

_____

_____

_____

_____

_____

_____

_____

_____

1. JAPAN: THE IMPERIAL AGE

As you read this section, complete the following outline to describe the development of imperial government in Japan between 600 and 1000 C.E.

I. Japan: The Imperial Age

  A. Taika Reforms

    1.

    2.

    3.

  B.

    1.

    2.

  C.

    1.

    2.

    3.

    4.

  D.

    1.

    2.

    3.

  E..

    1.

    2.

2. THE ERA OF WARRIOR DOMINANCE

As you read this section in your textbook, complete the concept web below to identify important characteristics of the society and culture of Japan during the "Era of Warrior Dominance."

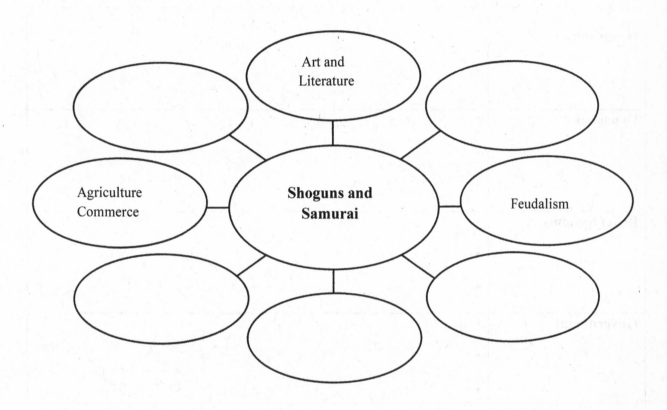

3. KOREA: BETWEEN CHINA AND JAPAN

As you read this section in your textbook, complete the chart below to identify important ideas about Korea.

FOCUS QUESTION: *How are Korea's history and culture linked to those of China and Japan?*

Geography	• • •
Dynasties	• • •
Belief Systems	• • •
Government	• • •
Invasions	• • •
Arts and Learning	• • •

Using the information in your chart, write a brief answer to the Focus Question.

4. KOREA: BETWEEN CHINA AND JAPAN

As you read this section in your textbook, complete the concept web included below to identify important components of the "sinification" of Korea, that is, the adoption of Chinese culture in Korea. Some items have been completed for you.

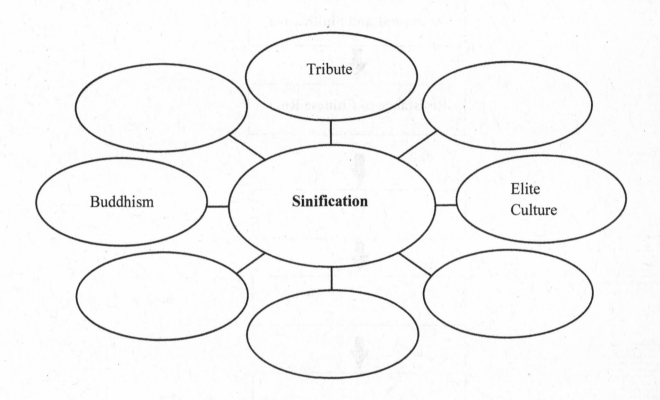

5. BETWEEN CHINA AND SOUTHEAST ASIA: THE MAKING OF VIETNAM

As you read this section in your textbook, complete the flow chart below to trace the development of Vietnam from the second century B.C.E. and the beginning of sinification to the struggle between the Nguyen and the Trinh for control of Vietnam from the sixteenth through the eighteenth centuries.

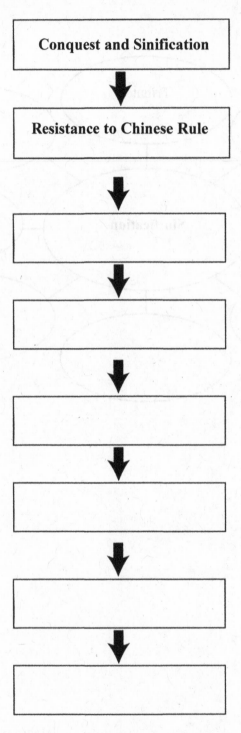

CHAPTER REVIEW

TERMS, EVENTS, PEOPLE

The following terms, people, and events are important to your understanding of the chapter. Define each one.

Taika reforms

Heian

Tale of Genji

Fujiwara

Bushi

Samurai

Seppuku

Gumpei wars

Bakufu

Shoguns

Hojo

Ashikaga Takuaji

Daimyos

Choson

Koguryo

Sinification

Silla

Yi

Trung sisters

Khmers and Chams

Nguyen

MY KEY TERMS

Write down terms that are unfamiliar. How are the words used? Do other words or examples reveal their meaning? Try to figure out meaning from the context.

Write the word or phrase that best completes the statement or answers the question.

1. The _____ reforms of 646 represented the culmination of centuries of Japanese borrowing from China and attempted to remake the Japanese monarch into an absolute ruler.

2. Written by Lady Murasaki, _____ was the first Japanese novel.

3. The _____ were aristocratic Japanese of the 9th century, who exercised exceptional influence over imperial affairs.

4. The military government established by the Minamoto following their defeat of the Taira was called the _____.

5. _____ were military leaders of the military government established by the Minamoto.

6. The _____ were warlord rulers of three hundred small states established following the disruption of the Ashikaga Shogunate.

7. The earliest kingdom in Korea, _____, was conquered by the Han emperor Wudi in 109 B.C.E.

8. _____ is the extensive adaptation of Chinese culture in other regions, particularly in Japan and Korea.

9. The Hanoi-based dynasty of the North that ruled during the period of Vietnamese expansion was the _____.

10. The dynasty that emerged in the frontier areas of southern Vietnam and who challenged the Hanoi-based dynasty was the _____.

MULTIPLE CHOICE REVIEW

Choose the one alternative that best completes the statement or answers the question.

1. How was Japan's relationship to China different from that of Korea and Vietnam?
a. Japan never received Confucianism from China.
b. Unlike the other regions, Japan retained the Confucian bureaucracy throughout the postclassical period.
c. Japan rejected Buddhism in favor of strictly Japanese animism.
d. Unlike the other regions, China never directly ruled Japan.

2. What was the central purpose of the Taika reforms?
a. to remake the Japanese monarch into an absolutist Chinese-style emperor
b. to destroy the Confucian scholar-gentry in favor of a military aristocracy
c. to increase the power of the Buddhist monastic structure
d. the destruction of the traditional peasant-conscript army

3. During the Heian period, members of the aristocracy
a. gained their position primarily by birth
b. lost their right to build up rural estates
c. played little role in the military
d. were excluded from the bureaucracy

4. The *Tale of Genji* described
a. the military organization of the *bakufu* in Kamakura.
b. life at the imperial court at Heian.
c. the structure of society under the Ashikaga Shogunate.
d. the travels of an imperial emissary in China.

5. Which of the following statements concerning the provincial military elite in Japan is *NOT* correct?
a. Provincial elite families often arose from local landowners and estate managers.
b. The provincial elite came to control land and labor and to deny these resources to the imperial government.
c. The rise of the provincial elite corresponded to the recovery of the imperial government and its overthrow of the aristocracy of the court.
d. Within their little kingdoms, warrior leaders administered law and collected revenue.

6. Which of the following statements concerning the nature of warfare among the bushi is most accurate?
a. The bushi depended on infantry tactics, equipping the samurai with long spears.
b. The introduction of gunpowder allowed the bushi to rely on artillery.
c. Battles hinged on massed assaults predicated on the willingness of retainers to sacrifice themselves.
d. Battles hinged on man-to-man duels of great champions typical of the heroic stage of combat.

7. The rise of the samurai in provincial Japanese society
a. reduced peasants to the status of serfs bound to the land they worked.
b. produced greater social mobility among the higher ranks of the peasantry.
c. frustrated the development of artisan and merchant classes.
d. created a class of free farmers with private land holdings throughout Japan.

8. The end of the Gempei Wars signaled the beginning of
a. the centralized Confucian bureaucracy.
b. the Japanese feudal age.
c. the Tokugawa Shogunate.
d. the Ashikaga Shogunate.

9. Which of the following was *NOT* a result of the growth of power of the provincial warrior elite in Japan?
a. The relevance of Chinese precedents and institutions to the Japanese diminished.
b. The Confucian precept that warriors should dominate the social and political world was strengthened.
c. Pretensions to a heavenly mandate and centralized power became ludicrous.
d. The emergence of a scholar-gentry was stifled by the reassertion of aristocratic power and prerogatives.

10. One of the major reasons for the Chinese failure to assimilate the Vietnamese was
a. the unwillingness of the Vietnamese elite to accept Chinese military organization.
b. the lack of impact of Chinese cultural imports in the Vietnamese peasantry.
c. the absence of Buddhism in Vietnam.
d. the widespread cultural impact of European culture in Indochina by the 13th century.

READING REVIEW: MAKING CONNECTIONS

After reading and studying the chapter, review your understanding by answering each of the following questions, which emphasize important ideas within the chapter.

1. What led to the failure of the Taika reforms? What was the political result?

2. Describe the nature of Japanese government between the Gempei Wars and the Onin War.

3. What was the nature of Japanese society and economy during the period of the *daimyos*?

4. How was the Sinification of Korea accomplished? How did it affect the social development of Korea?

5. What accounts for the cultural differences between the Vietnamese and Chinese?

6. What was the nature of the Vietnamese government following the reestablishment of independence?

7. What were the common elements of Chinese culture passed to all three of the satellite civilizations?

8. How was East Asian civilization different from other postclassical civilizations in terms of cultural diffusion?

CHAPTER 14
The Last Great Nomadic Challenges: From Chinggis Khan to Timur

Complete the following exercises in order *as you read* the chapter.

INTRODUCTION

Chapter introductions are a valuable guide to the material you are about to read, telling you what topics will be covered and how they fit together. If you keep the "big picture" provided by the introduction in mind as you read the chapter, you will find it much easier to organize your notes, identify important information, and avoid getting lost in the details. With this in mind, re-read the introduction to Chapter 14. As you read, make a list of the key topics you expect to learn about.

Key Topics

_____

_____

_____

_____

_____

_____

_____

_____

_____

_____

_____

_____

_____

_____

_____

_____

_____

_____

1. THE TRANSCONTINENTAL EMPIRE OF CHINGGIS KHAN

As you read this section of your textbook, create a timeline of the key events in the life of Chinggis Khan. Use the timeline included below as a starting point.

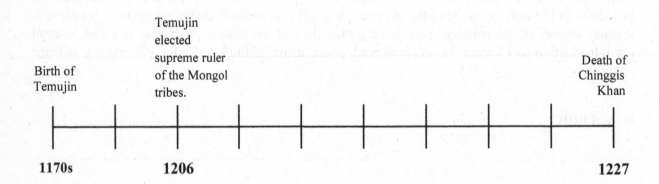

2. THE TRANSCONTINENTAL EMPIRE OF CHINGGIS KHAN

As you read this section of your textbook, complete the concept web to summarize the key aspects of military and administrative organization established by Chinggis Khan.

Military Organization	Administration
• _____ _____	• _____ _____
• _____ _____	• _____ _____
• _____ _____	• _____ _____
• _____ _____	• _____ _____

3. THE MONGOL DRIVE TO THE WEST

As you read this section of your textbook, take notes on the three main campaigns that comprised the Mongol drive to the West using the table included below.

Russia	Europe	Islamic Heartland
•	•	•
•	•	•
•	•	•
•	•	•

4. THE MONGOL INTERLUDE IN CHINESE HISTORY

As you read this section of your textbook, fill in the Venn diagram below to identify key differences between Mongol and Chinese culture, as well areas where the two cultures merged.

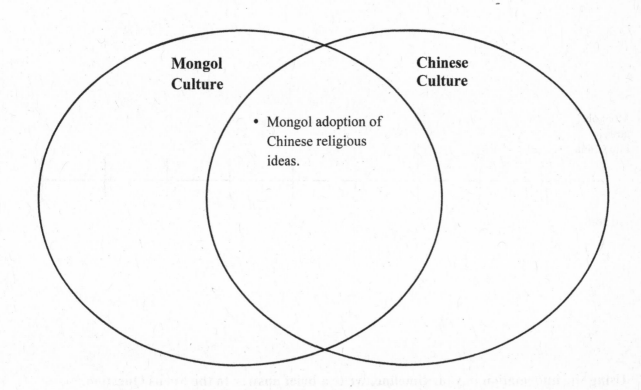

5. THE MONGOL INTERLUDE IN CHINESE HISTORY

As you read this section of your textbook, complete the timeline below to record important events during the Mongol and Ming empires.

FOCUS QUESTION: *What were the effects of the Mongol invasion and the rise of the Ming dynasty on China?*

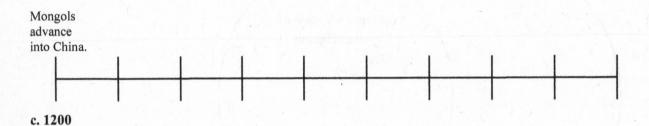

Mongols
advance
into China.

c. 1200

Using the information in your timeline, write a brief answer to the Focus Question.

TERMS, EVENTS, PEOPLE

The following terms, people, and events are important to your understanding of the chapter. Define each one.

Chinggis Khan

Tumens

Tangut

Muhammad Shah II

Karakorum

Shamanistic religion

Batu

Ogedei

Golden Horde

Prester John

Ilkhan khanate

Hulegu

Mamluks

Kubilai Khan

Tatu

Chabi

Nestorians.

Romance of the West Chamber

White Lotus Society

Ju Yuanzhang

Timur-i Lang

MY KEY TERMS

Write down terms that are unfamiliar. How are the words used? Do other words or examples reveal their meaning? Try to figure out meaning from the context.

Write the word or phrase that best completes the statement or answers the question.

1. The _____ was one of the four regional subdivisions of the Mongol Empire after the death of Chinggis Khan and covered much of what is today south-central Russia.

2. One of the four regional subdivisions of the Mongol Empire after Chinggis Khan's death, the _____ khanate eventually conquered much of the Abbasid Empire.

3. Prince _____ saved the city of Novgorod from the Mongols by submitting to Mongol demands.

4. _____ was the name given to a mythical, rich, and powerful Christian monarch whose kingdom had supposedly been cut off from Europe by the Muslim conquests.

5. _____, ruler of the Ilkhan khanate, was responsible for the capture and destruction of Baghdad.

6. The Mongols were finally defeated in the Middle East by the armies of the _____, a slave dynasty of Egypt.

7. The influential wife of Kubilai Khan, _____, promoted the interests of Buddhists in China.

8. The most famous dramatic work of the Yuan period was _____, indicative of the continued literary vitality of China during Mongol rule.

9. Secret religious sects, such as the _____, were dedicated to the overthrow of the Yuan dynasty.

10. A man from an impoverished peasant family, _____, emerged to found the Ming dynasty.

Choose the one alternative that best completes the statement or answers the question.

1. During what period did the Mongols have their greatest impact on China?
a. 907 to 1194
b. 1115 to 1250
c. 1215 to 1368
d. 1336 to 1405

2. Which of the following statements concerning the nomadic society of the Mongols prior to the establishment of empire is *not* accurate?
a. The Mongols were primarily herders of cattle and horses.
b. The basic social unit of the Mongols was the tribe.
c. Mongol leaders were selected by all free males for as long as they could hold power.
d. The Mongols were capable of forming tribal confederations in times of war.

3. *Tumens* were
a. consultative assemblies at which Mongolian leaders were selected.
b. rulers of Mongolian tribes.
c. the tents in which Mongols traditionally lived.
d. military units within the Mongol armies.

4. What tactic was frequently used by Chinggis Khan's troops on the field of battle?
a. frontal assault by massed heavy cavalry
b. massed artillery barrage followed by infantry attacks on the flanks
c. trench warfare
d. pretended flight to draw out the enemy followed by heavy cavalry attacks on the flanks

5. Which of the following reforms was *not* established by Chinggis Khan?
a. A script was devised for the Mongolian language to facilitate keeping records.
b. A legal code was promulgated to prevent feuds between Mongol clans.
c. Chinese and Islamic bureaucrats were banned from service in the Mongolian bureaucracy.
d. Farmers were taxed to support the Mongol courts and military expeditions.

6. At the time of the Mongol invasion, Russia
a. was part of the Byzantine Empire.
b. was united under the kings of Kiev.
c. had launched a series of successful assaults on the Islamic territories of the Abbasid dynasty.
d. was divided into numerous petty kingdoms centered on trading cities.

7. The Mongol conquest of Russia is often credited with
a. the extreme political decentralization of Russia in subsequent centuries.
b. the dominance of Saint Petersburg in Russian politics.
c. the desire of Russian princes to centralize their control and minimize the limitations placed on their power by the landed nobility.
d. lack of urbanization in much of eastern Europe.

8. In addition to the destruction of the Abbasid political capital at Baghdad and the weakening of Muslim military strength, what significant impact did the Mongol conquest have on the Islamic heartland?
a. The destruction of cities from central Asia to the shores of the Mediterranean devastated the focal points of Islamic civilization.
b. The successful assault on the east African city-states weakened the international trading system.
c. Shi'ism was eliminated as a major factor within Islam.
d. Much of the population of the Islamic heartland was converted to the animistic religion common among the Mongols.

9. Which of the following was *not* a method used by the Yuan to maintain the separation of Mongols and Chinese?
a. Chinese were forbidden to serve at any level in the Yuan administration.
b. Chinese scholars were forbidden to learn the Mongol script.
c. Mongols were forbidden to marry ethnic Chinese.
d. Only women from nomadic families were selected to the imperial harem.

10. In order to reduce the power of the scholar-gentry in China, the Yuan
a. ordered the burning of all Confucian books.
b. refused to reinstate the examination system for the civil service.
c. recognized Daoism as the state religion of China.
d. confiscated all land belonging to members of the intellectual elite.

READING REVIEW: MAKING CONNECTION

After reading and studying the chapter, review your understanding by answering each of the following questions, which emphasize important ideas within the chapter.

1. What was the impact of the Mongol conquest of Russia? Of the Islamic heartlands?

2. What was the impact of the Mongol conquest on Chinese social and political structure?

3. Overall, what were the positive aspects of the Mongol conquests? What were the negative aspects?

4. How did the conquests of Timur-i Lang contrast with those of the Mongols?

CHAPTER 15
The World in 1450: Changing Balance of World Power

Complete the following exercises in order *as you read* the chapter.

INTRODUCTION

Chapter introductions are a valuable guide to the material you are about to read, telling you what topics will be covered and how they fit together. If you keep the "big picture" provided by the introduction in mind as you read the chapter, you will find it much easier to organize your notes, identify important information, and avoid getting lost in the details. With this in mind, re-read the introduction to Chapter 15. As you read, make a list of the key topics you expect to learn about.

Key Topics

_____

_____

_____

_____

_____

_____

_____

_____

_____

_____

_____

_____

_____

_____

_____

_____

_____

_____

1. KEY CHANGES IN THE MIDDLE EAST

As you read this section of your textbook, use the table included below to take notes on the changes in the Middle East that facilitated the rise of the West as a global power.

Imperial Decline	Social and Cultural Change	Absence of International Leadership	China's Inward Turn

2. THE RISE OF THE WEST

As you read this section of your textbook, make a list like the one included below of the key factors that help explain the rise of the West to global prominence from the sixteenth century forward.

Rise of the West
1. Political centralization
2. Urbanization and commercial expansion
3. Technological innovation
4.
5.
6.
7.
8.

3. THE RISE OF THE WEST

As you read this section in your textbook, complete the following concept web to identify main ideas about the Italian Renaissance.

FOCUS QUESTION: *What were the ideals of the Renaissance, and how did Italian artists and writers reflect these ideals?*

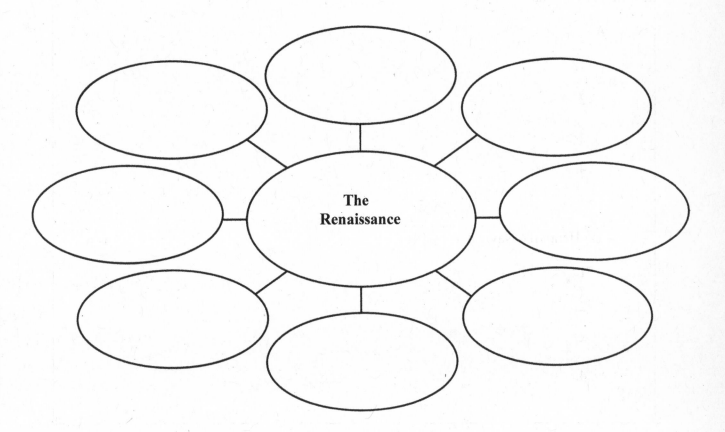

The
Renaissance

Using the information from your concept web, write a brief answer to the Focus Question.

4. WESTERN EXPANSION: THE EXPERIMENTAL PHASE

As you read this section of your textbook, complete the following outline to describe the initial steps taken by the Portuguese towards expansion beyond Europe.

I. Colonial Patterns

    A.

        1.

        2.

        3.

        4.

        5.

    B. Henry the Navigator

        1.

        2.

        3.

        4.

5. OUTSIDE THE WORLD NETWORK

As you read this section of your textbook, take notes on developments and their consequences in regions outside of the world network using the table included below.

	Developments	Long-Term Consequences
Aztecs and Incas	Political overextension	Imperial weakness
Polynesians: Hawaii		
Polynesians: New Zealand		

TERMS, EVENTS, PEOPLE

The following terms, people, and events are important to your understanding of the chapter. Define each one.

Ottoman Empire

Ibn-Rushd (Averroës)

Ming Dynasty

Zhenghe

Black Death

Renaissance

Portugal, Castile, and Aragon

Francesco Petrarch

Vivaldi brothers

Vasco da Gama

Henry the Navigator

Ethnocentrism

MY KEY TERMS

Write down terms that are unfamiliar. How are the words used? Do other words or examples reveal their meaning? Try to figure out meaning from the context.

Write the word or phrase that best completes the statement or answers the question.

1. The _____ was a Turkic government established in Asia Minor and eventually spreading throughout the Middle East following the retreat of the Mongols.

2. The _____ dynasty was established in China following the overthrow of the Mongol Yuan dynasty.

3. The cultural and political movement that begin in Italy circa 1400 and that created a literary and an artistic style with distinctly more secular priorities was called the _____.

4. Two kingdoms of the Iberian Peninsula, _____ , pressed the reconquest of Spain from the Muslims.

5. One of the earliest major literary figures of the Western Renaissance, _____ , was an Italian author and humanist.

6. Two Genoese brothers who attempted to find a western route to the "Indies," the _____, disappeared in 1291.

7. The first cash crop introduced in the Americas to be imported by Europe was _____, which had previously been imported from Asia.

8. The Polynesians who migrated to New Zealand, the _____, successfully adapted to a colder and harsher climate than that of their original homeland.

9. The _____, with their interlocking holdings in Eurasia, actively encouraged international travelers and exchanges of technology.

10. Despite its political and commercial roots, the Renaissance was first and foremost a(n) _____ movement.

Choose the one alternative that best completes the statement or answers the question.

1. Which of the following was *NOT* a symptom of the decline of the Abbasid caliphate by 1300?
a. the narrowing of intellectual life symbolized by the triumph of religion over literature, philosophy, and science
b. landlords seizing power over peasants
c. the decline of the Sufis
d. the decline of tax revenues for the state

2. What was the political state of the Middle East following the fall of the Abbasid Empire and the withdrawal of the Mongols?
a. The Ottoman Empire soon mastered most of the lands of the old caliphate.
b. The political fragmentation of the Middle East lasted for several centuries.
c. The Mongol conquests of the Middle East eliminated any form of centralized government until the 17th century.
d. The Middle East rapidly fell to the remaining Crusader states.

3. Which of the following statements concerning the Ottoman Empire is most accurate?
a. Turkish rulers did not promote maritime trade as vigorously as had the Arabs.
b. Scientific and philosophical investigations reached the level of innovation that they had enjoyed under the Abbasids.
c. The Turks refused to patronize the traditional Persian artists and craftsmen.
d. The Ottomans were more interested in cultural patronage than in military organization.

4. How long did the Ming dynasty sponsor commercial voyages in the 15th century?
a. five years
b. 12 years
c. 28 years
d. 57 years

5. Which of the following statements concerning state-sponsored trade in China is most accurate?
a. The cessation of trade severely damaged the internal economy of China.
b. The end of international trade signaled a general decentralization of government in China.
c. Because of Chinese dependence on imports from abroad, the decision to end the state sponsored expeditions was particularly critical in initiating cultural decline.
d. In Chinese terms, it was the brief trading flurry that was unusual, not its cessation.

6. Which of the following was *NOT* a drawback to the West's emergence as a global power?
a. lack of effective national and regional government
b. failure to establish key commercial and maritime links until after 1600
c. the attack on the Catholic Church, one of the organizing institutions of Western culture
d. economic crises among ordinary Europeans

7. What impact did the Mongols have on the rise of the West as a global power?
a. Their invasion of Western Europe delayed technological development in the West.
b. Mongol scientific and technological innovations were quickly adopted in the West.
c. The Mongols ended the threat posed to Europe by the Ottoman Empire..
d. Western Europe had access to Mongol trade routes but was not conquered and disrupted by the Mongols.

8. Which of the following is correctly associated with the Renaissance?
a. acceptance of Aristotle as the primary authority from the classical world
b. greater interest in nature and things of this world
c. disinterest in classical models
d. Gothic architecture

9. Why did the West have a negative balance of trade in 1400?
a. The West traded only with the poorer regions of Russia and Scandinavia.
b. Western elites purchased luxuries from the East, but had nothing to exchange other than gold.
c. Because the West generated little demand for products from other regions, the price paid was inordinately high.
d. The Mongols controlled all trade routes and charged high tariffs on all Western goods.

10. Which of the following is a common element of the Polynesian societies of Hawaii and New Zealand?
a. climate
b. centralized kingdoms
c. lack of metallurgy
d. lack of animal husbandry

READING REVIEW: MAKING CONNECTIONS

After reading and studying the chapter, review your understanding by answering each of the following questions, which emphasize important ideas within the chapter.

1. What were the signs of decline in the Middle East and China? Were there no signs of expansion or recovery in these areas?

2. What accounts for the relative rise of the West?

3. Describe the nature of the Italian Renaissance. In what way was it a strictly Italian experience? How was it important as a foundation for Western expansion?

4. What was the nature of the early Western exploration and colonial patterns?

5. What accounts for the relative decline of civilizations outside the world network?

6. Summarize the changes taking place in the world around 1400.

Complete the following exercises in order *as you read* the chapter.

INTRODUCTION

Chapter introductions are a valuable guide to the material you are about to read, telling you what topics will be covered and how they fit together. If you keep the "big picture" provided by the introduction in mind as you read the chapter, you will find it much easier to organize your notes, identify important information, and avoid getting lost in the details. With this in mind, re-read the introduction to Chapter 16. As you read, make a list of the key topics you expect to learn about.

Key Topics

_____

_____

_____

_____

_____

_____

_____

_____

_____

_____

_____

_____

_____

_____

_____

_____

_____

_____

1. THE WEST'S FIRST OUTREACH: MARITIME POWER

As you read this section in your textbook, use the table included below to take notes on the early expansion efforts of Portugal, Spain, England, and the Netherlands.

Western Maritime Expansion			
Portugal	**Spain**	**England**	**The Netherlands**
• 1434—Portugal moves south down the African coast.			

2. THE WEST'S FIRST OUTREACH: MARITIME POWER

As you read this section in your textbook, complete the following flowchart to identify causes and effects of European exploration.

FOCUS QUESTION: *How did the search for spices lead to global exploration?*

Reasons to Explore	Portugal Leads	Columbus Sails West
•	•	•
•	•	•
•	•	•

Using the information in your flowchart, write a brief answer to the Focus Question.

3. THE WEST'S FIRST OUTREACH: MARITIME POWER

As you read this section in your textbook, complete the following timeline of key explorations to help you sequence events that led to European empires in the Americas.

Key Explorations Leading to European Empires in the Americas	
1400s	Henry the Navigator

4. TOWARDS A WORLD ECONOMY

As you read this section in your textbook, complete the concept web below to describe key elements in the emergence of a new world economy in the sixteenth and seventeenth centuries.

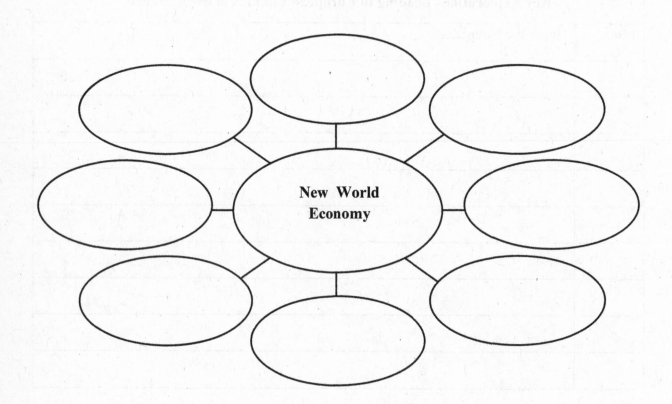

5. TOWARDS A WORLD ECONOMY

As you read this section of your textbook, complete the following flowchart to record the sequence events that led to the Columbian Exchange, as well as the effects.

Causes	Columbian Exchange	Effects
• Age of Exploration begins	•	•
•	•	•
•	•	•

6. COLONIAL EXPANSION

As you read this section of your textbook, use the table included below to compare and contrast European expansion in the Americas, Africa and Asia.

The Americas	Africa	Asia
•	•	•
•	•	•
•	•	•

7. COLONIAL EXPANSION

As you read this section in your textbook, complete the flowchart below to identify causes and effects of European exploration in Africa and Asia.

FOCUS QUESTION: *How did European nations build empires in Africa and Asia?*

Portugal	Netherlands	Spain	Britain
•	•	•	•
•	•	•	•

Using the information from your flowchart, write a brief answer to the Focus Question.

TERMS, EVENTS, PEOPLE

The following terms, people, and events are important to your understanding of the chapter. Define each one.

Vasco Da Gama

Christopher Columbus

Ferdinand Magellan

East India Companies

World economy

Columbian Exchange

Lepanto

Core nations

Mercantilism

Dependent economic zones

Mestizos

Vasco de Balboa

Francisco Pizarro

New France

Atlantic colonies

Treaty of Paris

Cape Colony

Boers

Calcutta

Seven Years' War

MY KEY TERMS

Write down terms that are unfamiliar. How are the words used? Do other words or examples reveal their meaning? Try to figure out meaning from the context.

Write the word or phrase that best completes each statement or answers the question.

1. In the 15th century, Portuguese sailors ventured around the _____, planning to find India and reach the eastern African coast.

2. A Spanish expedition under _____ set sail westward in 1519 and eventually sailed around the world.

3. The Dutch and British _____ were semiprivate companies, formed by pooling merchant capital and amassing great fortunes in commerce in Asia.

4. Even in Japan, where a firm isolationist policy was launched after 1600, Dutch traders secured special access to the port of _____.

5. The rulers of India's new _____ Empire in the 16th century were interested in some contact with Western traders.

6. The Dutch established a settlement called _____ in 1652 at the Cape of Good Hope to provide a coastal station for the Dutch sea-borne empire.

7. Only after 1770 did the expanding settlements of the Dutch _____ directly conflict with the Bantu farmers, opening a long battle for control of southern Africa.

8. British and French rivalry over control of India culminated in outright warfare in 1744 during the _____.

9. The _____ colonies of Britain in North America differed from other settlements in that they operated their own assemblies and developed internal trade.

10. Under the terms of the _____, which in 1763 settled the Seven Years War, France lost its colonies in North America, but regained its West Indian sugar islands.

MULTIPLE CHOICE REVIEW

Choose the one alternative that best completes the statement or answers the question.

1. Which of the following was *NOT* a part the growing importance of silver after 1500?
a. Spain was able to build a large army and major new public works projects.
b. Europeans used the silver primarily to invest in industrial development.
c. The Ming Dynasty in China began demanding periodic tax payments paid in silver.
d. The work force of conscripted Indian laborers at the Potosi mines grew to 150,000.

2. Prince Henry the Navigator
a. invented the astrolabe.
b. discovered Brazil.
c. rounded the Cape of Good Hope and eventually sailed to India.
d. directed a series of expeditions along the African coast and outward to the Azores.

3. Which of the following is one of the reasons the initiative in early conquest and exploration passed from northern European nations in the later 16th century?
a. Spain and Portugal were defeated in a critical war with the Ottoman Empire.
b. The Dutch and British improved the design of seagoing vessels, producing faster ships than their Iberian rivals.
c. Famine and disease catastrophically reduced Iberian populations after 1588.
d. The victory of the Spanish Armada over England forced that nation to seek new markets in the Atlantic.

4. Which statement best describes the Dutch and British East India Companies?
a. They encouraged free trade among the many regions of the growing European empires.
b. They held important trade monopolies and acted almost as independent governments in the lands that they claimed.
c. They were tightly controlled by their home governments.
d. They focused on commerce and generally avoided involving themselves in local governments.

5. Which of the following statements most accurately describes the impact of European conquest on the indigenous peoples of North America?
a. The arrival of the Europeans increased the total population of the Americas without diminishing native populations.
b. After initial decreases associated with losses in battle, indigenous populations recovered.
c. European immigration caused a slight drop in population growth among indigenous peoples.
d. Native American population was devastated by the introduction of European diseases.

6. Which of the following statements accounts for the Spanish failure to hold a position of dominance in world trade?
a. The Spanish monarchy established a policy of isolation in the 17th century.
b. The Catholic Church argued against the establishment of a commercial mentality in Spain.
c. Spain's interests were increasingly directed toward the conquest of the Ottoman Empire.
d. Spain lacked a strong banking system and was unable to handle the increase in commerce.

7. Which of the following statements concerning the relationship between China and the world commercial network of the 16th and 17th centuries is *NOT* accurate?
a. China had ample political strength and economic sophistication to avoid dependent status.
b. China sought to limit its participation in international trade.
c. China became dependent on large imports of European firearms.
d. China depended on extensive government regulation to keep European activities in check.

8. The earliest European colonies in the Americas were generally established by
a. entrepreneurs seeking to establish plantations.
b. large scale military expeditions organized and run by European governments.
c. religious missionaries.
d. European adventurers seeking gold.

9. The British colonies in North America
a. developed a society much like those in the Latin American and Caribbean colonies.
b. had much smaller populations and economies than colonies in Latin America and the Caribbean.
c. quickly developed significant cultural achievements that rivaled those of Europe.
d. were generally isolated from intellectual developments in Europe.

10. In Asia, significant conversion to Christianity
a. occurred only in the Philippines.
b. was limited to the Dutch holdings in Indonesia.
c. happened wherever the Westerners were able to establish colonies.
d. failed to occur anywhere.

READING REVIEW: MAKING CONNECTIONS

After reading and studying the chapter, review your understanding by answering each of the following questions, which emphasize important ideas within the chapter.

1. What technological innovations made the global dominance of the West possible?

2. Describe the early exploration of the world by the West.

3. What was the Colombian exchange?

4. How did British and French North America differ from other European colonies?

5. What were the results of the creation of a world economy?

6. How did non-European peoples respond to European expansion?

CHAPTER 17
The Transformation of the West 1450–1740

Complete the following exercises in order *as you read* the chapter.

INTRODUCTION

Chapter introductions are a valuable guide to the material you are about to read, telling you what topics will be covered and how they fit together. If you keep the "big picture" provided by the introduction in mind as you read the chapter, you will find it much easier to organize your notes, identify important information, and avoid getting lost in the details. With this in mind, re-read the introduction to Chapter 17. As you read, make a list of the key topics you expect to learn about.

Key Topics

_____

_____

_____

_____

_____

_____

_____

_____

_____

_____

_____

_____

_____

_____

_____

_____

_____

_____

1. THE FIRST BIG CHANGES: CULTURE AND COMMERCE, 1450-1650

As you read this section in your textbook, create a timeline of key events in Europe between 1450 and 1650.

Europe During the Renaissance and Reformation	
1450	Italian Renaissance is in full flowering.
1650	The era of religious wars comes to an end.

2. THE COMMERCIAL REVOLUTION

As you read this section of your textbook, take notes on the social and economic consequences of Europe's participation in the world economy in a table like the one included below.

Economic Consequences	Social Consequences
• Price inflation	• Emergence of a new proletariat
•	•
•	•
•	•
•	•

3. THE SCIENTIFIC REVOLUTION: THE NEXT PHASE OF CHANGE

As you read this section in your textbook, complete the table below to identify important thinkers of the Scientific Revolution, as well as their key contributions.

Thinkers of the Scientific Revolution	
Nicolaus Copernicus	
Johannes Kepler	
Galileo Galileo	

4. POLITICAL CHANGE

As you read this section in your textbook, compare and contrast the basic features of absolute and parliamentary monarchies in a table like the one included below.

Absolute Monarchies	Parliamentary Monarchies
• Centralization of power in the hands of the monarch	• Kings share power with representative assemblies
•	•
•	•
•	•

5. THE WEST BY 1750

As you read this section in your textbook, complete the concept web included below to identify important characteristics of the society and culture of eighteenth-century Europe.

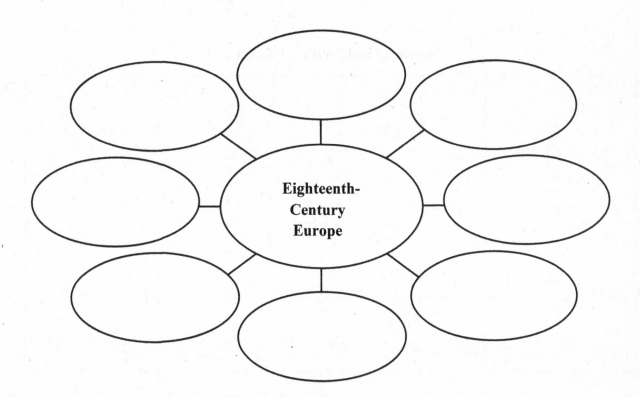

6. THE WEST BY 1750

As you read this section in your textbook, complete the concept web included below to identify the main ideas about as Enlightenment ideas spread across Europe, what cultural and political changes took place?

FOCUS QUESTION: *How did Enlightenment ideas spread across Europe?*

Cultural and Political Changes	

Using the information in your chart, write a brief answer to the Focus Question.

TERMS, EVENTS, PEOPLE

The following terms, people, and events are important to your understanding of the chapter.
Write a brief definition of each.

Italian Renaissance

Niccolo Machiavelli

Humanism

Northern Renaissance

Francis I

Johannes Gutenberg

European-style family

Martin Luther

Protestantism

Anglican church

Jean Calvin

Catholic Reformation

Jesuits

Edict of Nantes

Thirty Years War

Treaty of Westphalia

English Civil War

Proletariat

Witchcraft persecution

Scientific Revolution

Copernicus

Johannes Kepler

Galileo

William Harvey

René Descartes

Isaac Newton

Deism

John Locke

Absolute monarchy

Louis XIV

Glorious Revolution

Frederick the Great

Enlightenment

Adam Smith

Mary Wollstonecraft

MY KEY TERMS

Write down terms that are unfamiliar. How are the words used? Do other words or examples reveal their meaning? Try to figure out meaning from the context.

Write the word or phrase that best completes each statement or answers the question.

1. Renaissance culture stressed themes of _____, a focus on humankind as the center of intellectual and artistic endeavor.

2. The _____ focused in France, the Low Countries, Germany, and England, opened up after 1450.

3. In 1517 a German monk named _____ nailed a document containing 95 theses to the door of the castle church in Wittenberg.

4. The general wave of religious dissent against the Catholic Church was called _____.

5. _____, a Frenchman who established a base in the Swiss city of Geneva, insisted on God's predestination as a basic religious principle.

6. Under the _____, church councils revived Catholic doctrine and refuted key Protestant tenets.

7. The _____ trials of the 16th century reflected new resentments against the poor and new uncertainties about religious truth.

8. The reigning economic theory called _____, held that governments should promote the internal economy in order to improve tax revenues and to limit imports from other nations.

9. The English civil wars produced a final political settlement in 1688, the so-called _____, in which parliament won basic sovereignty over the king.

10. The aftermath of the Scientific Revolution spilled over into a new movement known as the _____, centered particularly in France, but with adherents throughout the Western world.

Choose the one alternative that best completes the statement or answers the question.

1. The Italian Renaissance emphasized the themes of
a. Humanism.
b. Scholasticism.
c. Sophism.
d Mercantalism.

2. Which of the following accounts in part for the decline of the Italian Renaissance?
a. Venice's political unification of all of northern Italy
b. the Protestant Reformation
c. the invasion of the peninsula by France and Spain
d. the economic depression that ended artistic patronage

3. By the 16th century, at what age did most Europeans marry?
a. early teenage years
b. late teenage years
c. early twenties
d. late twenties

4. What was one of the primary differences between the Italian and Northern Renaissances?
a. The Northern Renaissance occurred a century earlier than the Italian Renaissance.
b. Northern humanists focused more on religion than their Italian counterparts.
c. There were no major literary figures in the Northern Renaissance.
d. The Northern Renaissance did not make use of the classical languages typical of the Italian Renaissance.

5. Which of the following statements most accurately describes popular support for Luther's religious movement?
a. German princes opposed Luther because he advocated the overthrow of their authority.
b. German princes who became Protestants could increase their independence from the emperor.
c. The poor supported Luther's movement in return for Luther's promise to redistribute land.
d. German merchants refused to support Lutheranism because the new religion was opposed to profit-making.

6. Which of the following was NOT a result of the Thirty Years' War?
a. It reduced German prosperity and power for a full century.
b. The treaty that ended the war established Spain as the principal power of western Europe.
c. The treaty that ended the war granted political independence to the Protestant Netherlands.
d. Some princely states in Germany chose one religion, some another.

7. Which of the following was characteristic of the commercial revolution of the 16th century?
a. Imports of American bullion led to a decline in prices in western Europe.
b. European nations progressively adopted free trade and dropped tariff systems.
c. The establishment of colonies led to increased foreign competition and a decline in European manufacturing.
d. The commercial revolution saw the formation of great trading companies which purchased monopolies of trade with specific regions or over specific commodities.

8. Louis XIV of France was associated with the form of government called
a. enlightened despotism.
b. corporatism.
c. feudal monarchy.
d. absolute monarchy.

9. Which of the following states stood apart from the trend toward absolute monarchy in the 17th century and retained a parliamentary regime?
a. France
b. Britain
c. Spain
d. Austria-Hungary

10. What crop introduced into Europe in the 17th century substantially improved the food supply?
a. cucumbers
b. peas
c. millet
d. potatoes

READING REVIEW: MAKING CONNECTIONS

The following questions are intended to emphasize important ideas within the chapter.

1. Between what dates did the major pattern of change in Western civilization occur? What are the major historical trends?

2. What are the major differences between the Italian Renaissance and the Northern Renaissance?

3. What Protestant churches were established by the Reformation? What was the nature of religious warfare?

4. Describe the causes and results of the commercial revolution.

5. What was the scientific revolution? What were some of the major discoveries?

6. How did the Scientific Revolution and the Enlightenment change popular culture and daily life?

CHAPTER **18**
The Rise of Russia

Complete the following exercises in order *as you read* the chapter.

INTRODUCTION

Chapter introductions are a valuable guide to the material you are about to read, telling you what topics will be covered and how they fit together. If you keep the "big picture" provided by the introduction in mind as you read the chapter, you will find it much easier to organize your notes, identify important information, and avoid getting lost in the details. With this in mind, re-read the introduction to Chapter 18. As you read, make a list of the key topics you expect to learn about.

Key Topics

_____

_____

_____

_____

_____

_____

_____

_____

_____

_____

_____

_____

_____

_____

_____

_____

_____

1. RUSSIA' EXPANSIONIST POLITICS UNDER THE TSARS

As you read this section of your textbook, take notes using the concept web below on the Mongol occupation of Russian civilization..

FOCUS QUESTION: *What were the effects of Mongol occupation on Russian civilization?*

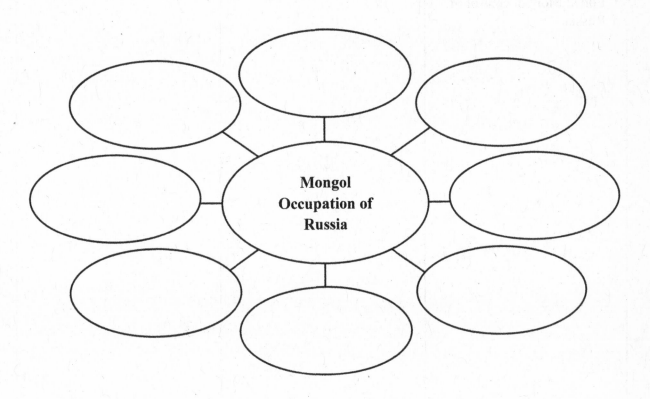

Mongol
Occupation of
Russia

Using the information your concept web, write a brief answer to the Focus Question.

2. RUSSIA'S EXPANSIONIST POLITICS UNDER THE TSARS

As you read this section of your textbook, take notes on Russian expansion under Ivan III, Ivan IV, and Michael Romanov using the table included below.

Russian Expansion		
Ivan III	**Ivan IV**	**Michael Romanov**
• Ended Mongol control of Russia		

3. Russia's First Westernization, 1690-1790

As you read this section in your textbook, complete the table below to identify the westernizing policies of Peter the Great and Catherine the Great, as well as the consequences of those policies.

FOCUS QUESTION: *How did Peter the Great and Catherine the Great strengthen Russia and expand its territory?*

Policies	Consequences
Peter the Great: Imitated Western military organization and formed secret police	Suppressed local militias and prevented dissent

Using the information in your table, write a brief answer to the Focus Question.

4. THEMES IN EARLY MODERN RUSSIAN HISTORY

As you read this section in your textbook, complete the following outline to describe themes in Early Modern Russian social development.

I. Serfdom: The Life of East Europe's Masses

    A. Demise of Russia's Free Peasantry

    B.

    C.

    D.

II. Eastern Agriculture, Trade and Economic Dependence

    A.

    B.

    C.

    D.

III. Social Unrest

    A.

    B.

    C.

    D.

IV. Russia and Eastern Europe

    A.

    B.

    C.

    D.

    E.

5. THEMES IN EARLY MODERN RUSSIAN HISTORY

As you read this section in your textbook, complete the concept web below to summarize the economic and social effects of the estate agricultural system.

Estate Agricultural System	
Economic Effects	**Social Effects**
•	•
•	•
•	•
•	•

6. THEMES IN EARLY MODERN RUSSIAN HISTORY

As you read this section in your textbook, complete the following Venn diagram to describe the similarities and differences between Russia and Eastern Europe during Early Modern Russian history.

FOCUS QUESTION: *How did the characteristics of Russia and Eastern Europe compare?*

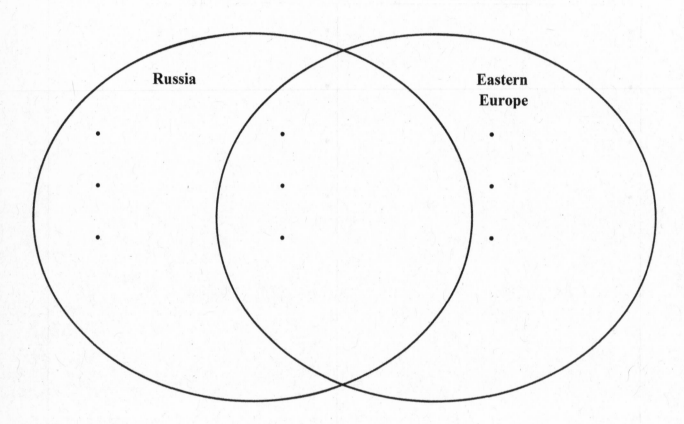

Using the information in your diagram, write a brief answer to the Focus Question.

CHAPTER REVIEW

TERMS, PEOPLE, EVENTS

The following terms, people, and events are important to your understanding of the chapter. Write a brief definition of each.

Population revolution

Proto-industrialization

American Revolution

French Revolution

Louis XVI

Declaration of the Rights of Man and the Citizen

Guillotine

Maximilien Robespierre

Napoleon Bonaparte

Congress of Vienna

Liberalism

Radicals

Socialism

Nationalism

Greek Revolution

French Revolution of 1830

Belgian Revolution of 1830

Reform Bill of 1832

James Watt

Factory system

French Revolution of 1848

Revolutions of 1848

Louis Pasteur

Benjamin Disraeli

Camillo di Cavour

Otto von Bismarck

American Civil War (1861–1865)

Social question

Karl Marx

Revisionism

Feminist movements

Mass leisure culture

Charles Darwin

Albert Einstein

Sigmund Freud

Romanticism

American exceptionalism

Triple Alliance

Triple Entente

Balkan nationalism

MY KEY TERMS

Write down terms that are unfamiliar. How are the words used? Do other words or examples reveal their meaning? Try to figure out meaning from the context.

SHORT ANSWER REVIEW

Write the word or phrase that best completes each statement or answers the question.

1. It was the _____ that most clearly set in motion the political restructuring of western Europe.

2. Thousands of people were executed during the _____, the radical phase of the French Revolution.

3. The final phase of the French Revolution was ushered in by the victory of _____, a leading general who soon converted the republic to an authoritarian empire.

4. _____ focused primarily on issues of political structure, as they sought ways to limit state interference in individual life.

5. _____ wanted wider voting rights and, in some cases, outright democracy.

6. The essence of the _____ was technological change, particularly the application of engines driven by coal to the production process.

7. Count _____ in the Italian state of Piedmont began to support industrial development and extend the powers of parliament to please liberal forces.

8. _____ held that emotion and impression, not reason and generalization, were the keys to the mysteries of human experience and nature itself.

9. Germany, Austria-Hungary, and Italy formed the _____.

10. Britain, Russia, and France constituted the _____.

Choose the one alternative that best completes the statement or answers the question.

1. Which of the following did Ivan IV *NOT* base his claim to be the legitimate ruler of central Asia on?
a. He was himself a descendent of the former Mongol rulers of central Asia.
b. He had defeated the Mongols, and thus he could take their place as "khan."
c. Central Asia was the long-standing property of the Rurik dynasty (his family).
d. It was his duty as a Christian leader to remove infidel rulers from power.

2. Ivan III was responsible for the
a. abolition of serfdom in Russia.
b. freeing much of Russia from the Mongols.
c. policies of Westernization that required changes in dress among the Russian elite.
d. conversion of Russia to Roman Catholicism.

3. Why did Russian expansion policy focus particularly on central Asia?
a. The Russians wished to seize control of the trade routes with China.
b. Most of the Russian population remained ethnically Mongol with cultural ties in Asia.
c. There were natural barriers to westward expansion.
d. The Russians were motivated by a desire to push the former Mongol overlords farther back to prevent renewed invasion.

4. Cossacks were
a. those who objected to reforms in the Orthodox Church.
b. members of the Russian nobility.
c. peasants recruited to migrate to newly seized lands in the Russian empire.
d. the designated heirs of the tsars.

5. Which of the following was *NOT* a policy of Alexis Romanov?
a. the abolition of the assemblies of nobles
b. the abolition of serfdom
c. resuming the Orthodox tradition of state control over the church
d. the continuation of colonization in central Asia

6. Peter the Great's creation of a new capital at St. Petersburg
a. followed the destruction of Moscow during the peasant rebellion.
b. demonstrated the continued emphasis of Russian expansion in central Asia.
c. was indicative of the desire to push the borders of Russia into the Balkans.
d. reflected the growing shift of Russian interests westward.

7. Where was Peter the Great's program of economic development concentrated?
a. cloth production
b. mining and metallurgical industries
c. urbanization
d. pottery production

8. The government of Catherine the Great
a. controlled all aspects of central and local administration.
b. advocated the abolition of serfdom and the reform of coercive labor systems in Russia.
c. was so hamstrung by peasant rebellion that it scarcely functioned by the end of the reign.
d. was strongly centralized but yielded virtually all local control to the nobility.

9. All of the following countries participated in the partition of Poland *EXCEPT*
a. Prussia.
b. Hungary.
c. Austria.
d. Russia.

10. In 1649, Russian serfdom
a. was abolished.
b. was converted to legal slavery.
c. began to modify to a free peasantry as the result of Westernization.
d. became hereditary.

READING REVIEW: MAKING CONNECTIONS

After reading and studying the chapter, review your understanding by answering each of the following questions, which emphasize important ideas within the chapter.

1. What was the nature of Russian expansion under Ivan III and Ivan IV?

2. What was the impact of Westernization under Peter the Great? What were its limitations?

3. What was the extent of Westernization under Catherine the Great? What were its limitations?

4. What was the nature of Russian serfdom? What was the "peasant problem"?

5. Why did Russia become economically dependent on the West?

CHAPTER 19
Early Latin America

Complete the following exercises in order *as you read* the chapter.

INTRODUCTION

Chapter introductions are a valuable guide to the material you are about to read, telling you what topics will be covered and how they fit together. If you keep the "big picture" provided by the introduction in mind as you read the chapter, you will find it much easier to organize your notes, identify important information, and avoid getting lost in the details. With this in mind, re-read the introduction to Chapter 19. As you read, make a list of the key topics you expect to learn about.

Key Topics

_____

_____

_____

_____

_____

_____

_____

_____

_____

_____

_____

_____

_____

_____

_____

_____

_____

_____

1. SPANIARDS AND PORTUGUESE: FROM RECONQUEST TO CONQUEST

As you read this section in your textbook, complete the following outline to describe initial phases of the Spanish conquest of the Americas.

I. Iberian Society and Tradition
   A. An Urban Society
   B.
   C.
   D.
   E.
II. The Chronology of Conquest
   A.
   B.
   C.
III. The Caribbean Crucible
   A.
   B.
   C.
   D.
IV. The Paths of Conquest
   A.
   B.
   C.
   D.
V.   The Conquerors
   A.
   B.
   C.
   D.

VI. Conquest and Morality
   A.
   B.
   C.
   D.

2. THE DESTRUCTION AND TRANSFORMATION OF INDIGENOUS SOCIETIES

As you read this section of your textbook, compare and contrast the systems of forced labor known as the *encomienda* and the *mita*.

Encomienda	Mita
The holder of an *encomienda* had the right to tax or extract labor from the people of a region.	The *mita* system was adapted from indigenous precedents.

3. COLONIAL ECONOMIES AND GOVERNMENTS

As you read this section of your textbook, use the table included below to take notes on the central activities and institutions of the Spanish empire in the New World.

Mining	Settlement Patterns	Industry and Commerce	The Church

4. BRAZIL: THE FIRST PLANTATION SOCIETY

As you read this section of your textbook, use the table included below to take notes on the impact of sugar production and gold mining on Brazilian society.

Sugar	Gold
• Brazil became the world's leading sugar producer in the seventeenth century.	• Brazil's first gold rush began in the late seventeenth century.

5. MULTIRACIAL SOCIETIES

As you read this section of your textbook, take notes on the three main ethnic categories in Iberian America using a table like the one included below.

FOCUS QUESTION: *What were the characteristics of the social hierarchy of the American colonies?*

African Slaves and Native Americans	Castas	Spaniards
Occupied lowest rung in social hierarchy	People of mixed ancestry	

6. THE 18-CENTURY REFORMS

As you read this section in your textbook, create a timeline of reform efforts and rebellions in eighteenth-century Latin America.

FOCUS QUESTION: *Why did the 18th-century reform efforts provoke colonial resistance?*

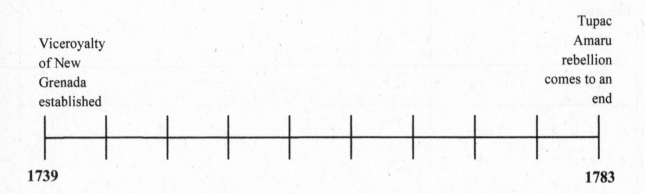

Viceroyalty of New Grenada established

Tupac Amaru rebellion comes to an end

1739

1783

CHAPTER REVIEW

TERMS, PEOPLE, EVENTS

The following terms, people, and events are important to your understanding of the chapter. Write a brief definition of each.

Ferdinand of Aragon and Isabella of Castile

Encomiendas

Hispaniola

Bartolomé de las Casas

Hernán Cortés

Moctezuma II

Mexico City

New Spain

Francisco Vácquez de Coronado

Pedro de Valdivia

Mita

Colombian Exchange

Potosí

Huancavelica

Haciendas

Consulado

Galleons

Treaty of Tordesillas

Recopilación

Council of the Indies

Letrados

Viceroyalties

Sor Juana Inés de la Cruz

Pedro Alvares Cabral

Paulistas

Minas Gerais

Rio de Janeiro

Sociedad de castas

Peninsulares

Creoles

Amigos del país

War of the Spanish Succession

Charles III

José de Galvez

Marquis of Pombal

Comunero Revolt

Tupac Amaru

MY KEY TERMS

Write down terms that are unfamiliar. How are the words used? Do other words or examples reveal their meaning? Try to figure out meaning from the context.

Write the word or phrase that best completes each statement or answers the question.

1. The Dominican friar _____ initiated the struggle for justice for Native Americans in Spanish colonies.

2. _____ was built by the Spaniards on the ruins of Tenochtitlan as the capital of New Spain.

3. Unlike the Spaniards in Mexico, when the Inca capital of Cuxco fell in 1533, the conquerors built their new capital of _____ closer to the coast.

4. In the sixteenth century, the *encomienda* was gradually replaced by the _____, a system of labor drafts.

5. Rural estates, or _____, producing primarily for consumers in America, became the basis of wealth and power for the local aristocracy in many regions.

6. The Spanish scholar _____ argued that Indians were not fully human and thus enslaving them was acceptable.

7. The Treaty of _____, signed in 1494 by Spain and Portugal, clarified the spheres of influence of the two nations.

8. The body of laws for the Indies was so large and varied that it took almost a century to complete a great law code, the _____.

9. In New Granada, popular complaints against the government's control of tobacco and liquor led to the widespread _____ Revolt in 1781.

10. In Peru, a great Indian uprising took place under the leadership of Jose Gabriel Condorcanqui, known as _____.

Choose the one alternative that best completes the statement or answers the question.

1. Which of the following is *NOT* characteristic of Iberian society?
a. heavy urbanization
b. the absence of slaveholding traditions
c. strong tradition of military conquests
d. long contact with Islamic civilization

2. What was the *encomienda*?
a. grants of Indians to individual Spaniards in a form of serfdom
b. the local administrative unit of the Latin American colonies
c. agricultural settlements in Peru
d. the legal code imposed on the Spanish colonies

3. The tremendous decline of the Indian population was matched by the rapid increase in
a. technological development.
b. European livestock.
c. Spanish women.
d. imports of cotton cloth.

4. By the mid-16th century, which of the following statements concerning the Spanish colonies was most accurate?
a. Trade to the Spanish colonies was entirely within the hands of English merchants.
b. Trade to the American colonies was limited to Spanish merchants, but otherwise unrestricted.
c. The self-sufficiency of the colonies meant that there was little commerce between Europe and Latin America.
d. Trade to the American colonies was managed by the Board of Trade, which funneled all commerce through Seville and Cadiz.

5. When the Spanish government moved to end the *encomienda* system, it worked to replace it with
a. a free labor system.
b. forced Indian labor extracted through local officials, a practice called the mita in Peru.
c. the enslavement of the Indian population.
d. immigrant labor from Europe.

6. Which of the following statements concerning the agricultural system of Latin America is *NOT* accurate?
a. Colonists faced with declining Indian populations found landownership more attractive.
b. In places where large sedentary populations existed, Indian communal agriculture of traditional crops continued.
c. Plantation crops like sugar and later cacao were exported to Europe in sufficient quantities to exceed the value of bullion exported.
d. Spanish America retained a predominantly agrarian economy.

7. In 1494, Spain and Portugal clarified the boundaries of their colonial possessions in the
a. Treaty of Tordesillas.
b. Treaty of Paris.
c. Treaty of Utrecht.
d. Treaty of Westphalia.

8. By 1700, slaves comprised approximately what proportion of the Brazilian population?
a. one-fourth
b. one-third
c. one-half
d. two-thirds

9. Which of the following statements concerning the Brazilian economy is most accurate?
a. The Brazilian model of estate agriculture based on slave labor could not be successfully duplicated elsewhere in the Americas.
b. The demographic decline of the Indian population eventually made the production of sugar impossible, and estate agriculture in Brazil disappeared.
c. Competition from English, French, and Dutch plantations in the Caribbean undercut the Brazilian sugar industry.
d. Because Brazil never developed a mining economy, sugar remained its most lucrative export.

10. Which of the following statements concerning the 18th-century Spanish reforms in America is most accurate?
a. The English system of justices of the peace was introduced to replace the *audiencias*.
b. The Spanish colonies were largely demilitarized.
c. The French intendancy system was introduced.
d. The Spanish reforms did little to alter the patterns of local administration.

After reading and studying the chapter, review your understanding by answering each of the following questions, which emphasize important ideas within the chapter.

1. What aspects of Iberian society were transferred to the New World colonies?

2. What model for American colonization was established in the Caribbean?

3. What was the nature of the exploitation of Indians in the Americas?

4. Discuss the nature of Spanish administration in the American colonies.

5. How did the discovery of gold change the economic organization of Brazil?

6. What was the nature of the 18th-century reforms in the Portuguese and Spanish colonies?

CHAPTER 20
Africa and the Africans in the Age of the Atlantic Slave Trade

Complete the following exercises in order *as you read* the chapter.

INTRODUCTION

Chapter introductions are a valuable guide to the material you are about to read, telling you what topics will be covered and how they fit together. If you keep the "big picture" provided by the introduction in mind as you read the chapter, you will find it much easier to organize your notes, identify important information, and avoid getting lost in the details. With this in mind, re-read the introduction to Chapter 20. As you read, make a list of the key topics you expect to learn about.

Key Topics

_____

_____

_____

_____

_____

_____

_____

_____

_____

_____

_____

_____

_____

_____

_____

_____

_____

_____

_____

1. AFRICA AND THE CREATION OF AN ATLANTIC SYSTEM

As you read this section of your textbook, complete the list below of the key developments in Africa during the seventeenth and eighteenth centuries.

Key Developments in Africa

1. Expansion of the slave trade

2. Participation in the Columbian exchange

3. Islam consolidated in Sudan and East Africa

4.

5.

6.

7.

8.

2. THE ATLANTIC SLAVE TRADE

As you read this section of your textbook, complete the flow chart below to trace the development of the African slave trade in the early modern period.

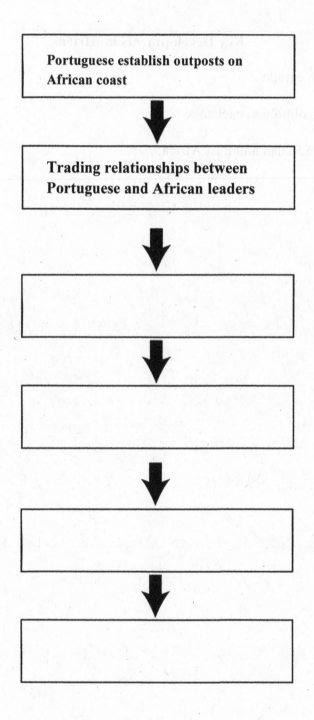

3. AFRICAN SOCIETIES, SLAVERY, AND THE SLAVE TRADE

As you read this section of your textbook, use the table below to take notes on the impact of the slave trade on Asante, Dahomey, East Africa, and Sudan.

Asante	Dahomey	East Africa	Sudan
•	•	•	•
•	•	•	•
•	•	•	•
•	•	•	•
•	•	•	•

4. AFRICAN SOCIETIES, SLAVERY, AND THE SLAVE TRADE

As you read this section, complete the concept web below to identify ways in which slaving impacted politics in Africa.

FOCUS QUESTION: *How did the slave trade influence African politics and the rise of states?*

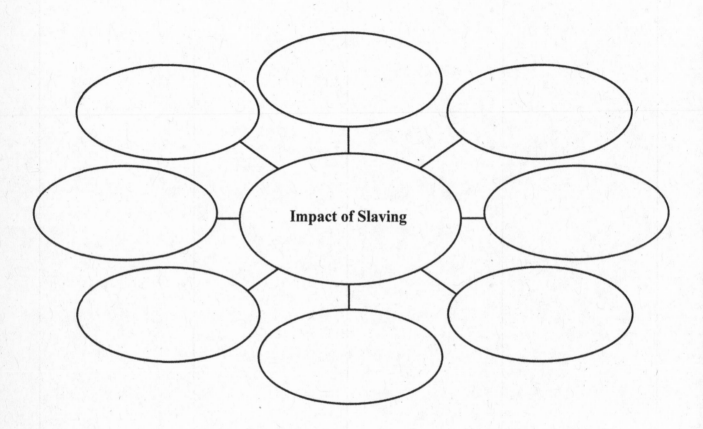

Using the information in your concept web, write a brief answer to the Focus Question.

5. WHITE SETTLERS AND AFRICANS IN SOUTHERN AFRICA

As you read this section of your textbook, complete the following outline to describe the interactions between white settlers and Africans in Southern Africa in the early modern period.

I. The Southern Bantu

    A. Society and Government

6. THE AFRICAN DIASPORA

As you read this section of your textbook, complete the following outline to describe African-influenced slave societies that developed in the Americas.

I. The Middle Passage

    A. Conditions

7. THE AFRICAN DIASPORA

As you read this section, take notes on the characteristics of African slavery and American slavery using the chart below.

FOCUS QUESTION: *How did African slavery differ from American slavery?*

African Slavery	American Slavery
•	•
•	•
•	•

Using the information in your chart, write a brief answer to the Focus Question.

8. THE AFRICAN DIASPORA

As you read the section in your textbook, complete the list below identifying the factors leading to the end of the slave trade.

FOCUS QUESTION: *Why did the slave trade come to an end?*

The End of the Slave Trade

1.

2.

3.

4.

5.

Using the information in your list, write a brief answer to the Focus Question.

TERMS, EVENTS, PEOPLE

The following terms, people, and events are important to your understanding of the chapter. Define each one.

Factories

El Mina

Nzinga Mvemba

Luanda

Royal African Company

Triangular trade

Asante

Osei Tutu

Asantehene

Benin

Dahomey

Usuman Dan Fodio

Great Trek

Shaka

Mfecane

Swazi and Lesotho

Middle Passage

Saltwater slaves

Obeah

Palmares

Surinam Maroons

MY KEY TERMS

Write down terms that are unfamiliar. How are the words used? Do other words or examples reveal their meaning? Try to figure out meaning from the context.

Write the word or phrase that best completes each statement or answers the question.

1. The most important of the Portuguese trade forts along the east African coast was _____, in the heart of the gold-producing region.

2. The Spanish developed a complicated system in which a healthy adult male slave was called a(n) "_____," while children and women were valued at fractions of that value.

3. During some periods in Africa, there did exist a(n) _____ trade in which slaves were carried to the Americas, sugar and tobacco to Europe, and European products to the coast of Africa.

4. A purifying Sufi variant of Islam had an intense impact on the _____ people, pastoralists who were spread across a broad area of the western Sudan.

5. The rise of the Zulu and other Nguni chiefdoms was the beginning of the _____, or wars of crushing and wandering.

6. _____ successfully resisted the Zulu example by combining Sotho and Nguni speakers and defending itself against Nguni armies.

7. The slave voyage to the Americas, the "_____" as it was called, was a traumatic experience for the slaves.

8. In the Brazilian _____ and in Haitian Vodun, rather fully developed versions of African religion flourished.

9. During the 17th century in Brazil, _____, an enormous runaway slave kingdom with numerous villages, resisted Portuguese and Dutch attempts to destroy it.

10. Under the leadership of _____, an abolitionist movement gained strength in Britain against its opponents made up of merchants and the "West Indies interests."

Choose the one alternative that best completes the statement or answers the question.

1. What European nation first established direct contact with sub-Saharan Africa?
a. Spain
b. England
c. Italy
d. Portugal

2. King Nzinga Mvemba of Kongo was noteworthy because he
a. was the first African monarch converted to Christianity.
b. successfully defeated the Portuguese at the battle of Kuwezi.
c. was one of the most powerful advocates of the African slave trade.
d. eventually conquered the Boers of southern Africa

3. Which of the following statements concerning slavery in Europe before 1450 is most accurate?
a. Europe never had a tradition of slavery.
b. Slavery had been extensive in the ancient world but had died out during the Middle Ages.
c. Slavery had died out during the Middle Ages in most of Europe except along the military frontier between Christians and Muslims in the Mediterranean.
d. Slavery was common everywhere in Europe during the Middle Ages.

4. Aside from Brazil, the region of the New World that received the most slaves was
a. the British colonies of the southern Atlantic.
b. Mexico.
c. the plantation islands of the Caribbean.
d. Chile.

5. What was the demographic impact of the slave trade on Africa?
a. The slave trade exported millions but the loss was made up in indigenous population increases.
b. Population in Africa seems to have grown at a higher than average rate.
c. The slave trade left central Africa with of a disproportionately high number of women.
d. As a result of the slave trade, the population of Africa was only one-third of what it would have been without the export of men and women.

6. What was the impact of the slave trade on Europeans sent to Africa?
a. European died in high number of tropical diseases.
b. Europeans established wealthy colonies that expanded through the 19th century.
c. Europeans rapidly dispersed throughout the African nations of the interior and intermarried with indigenous populations.
d. Europeans sent to Africa often remained for many years, absorbing the African cultures.

7. Which of the following was *NOT* a large African state that developed during the period of the Atlantic slave trade?
a. Asante
b. Benin
c. Dahomey
d. Ghana

8. Under whose rule was unity achieved among the numerous Akan clans of Asante?
a. Usuman Dan Fodio
b. Osei Tutu
c. Shaka
d. Agaja

9. The Sufi mystic responsible for initiating a religious reform movement among the Hausa kingdoms was
a. Usuman Dan Fodio.
b. Osei Tutu.
c. Shaka.
d. Agaja.

10. The "Middle Passage" referred to
a. the journey from captivity to the coastline of Africa.
b. the sale of slaves in the Americas and subsequent transportation to plantations.
c. the group of slaves permanently in rebellion in Suriname.
d. the voyage from Africa across the Atlantic to the Americas.

READING REVIEW: MAKING CONNECTIONS

After reading and studying the chapter, review your understanding by answering each of the following questions, which emphasize important ideas within the chapter.

1. What were the stages in the Portuguese penetration of Africa?

2. Trace the changes in volume of the slave trade between 1450 and 1850.

3. What was the demographic impact of the African slave trade on the sub-Saharan region?

4. How did the slave trade affect African state formation? Give examples.

5. What was the *mfecane*? How did it affect southern Africa?

6. What was the social structure of American slave-based societies?

CHAPTER 21
The Muslim Empires

Complete the following exercises in order *as you read* the chapter.

INTRODUCTION

Chapter introductions are a valuable guide to the material you are about to read, telling you what topics will be covered and how they fit together. If you keep the "big picture" provided by the introduction in mind as you read the chapter, you will find it much easier to organize your notes, identify important information, and avoid getting lost in the details. With this in mind, re-read the introduction to Chapter 21. As you read, make a list of the key topics you expect to learn about.

Key Topics

_____

_____

_____

_____

_____

_____

_____

_____

_____

_____

_____

_____

_____

_____

_____

_____

_____

_____

_____

_____

1. THE OTTOMANS: FROM FRONTIER WARRIORS TO EMPIRE BUILDERS

As you read this section in your textbook, take notes on the central features and institutions of the Ottoman Empire in a table like the one included below.

The Ottoman Empire			
The Military	**The Court**	**Constantinople: Trade and Commerce**	**Constantinople: Society and Culture**
• Ottoman economy and society geared to warfare			

2. THE OTTOMANS: FROM FRONTIER WARRIORS TO EMPIRE BUILDERS

As you read this section, complete the concept web below to summarize how the Ottomans built their vast empire.

FOCUS QUESTION: *What factors influenced the rise of the Ottoman?*

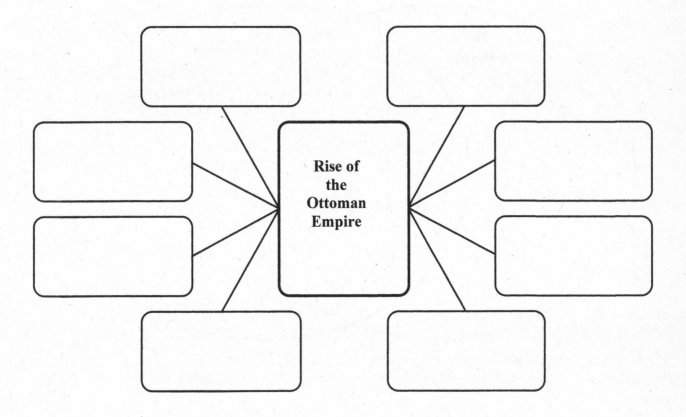

Using the information in your chart, write a brief answer to the Focus Question.

3. THE SHI'A CHALLENGE OF THE SAFAVIDS

As you read this section of your textbook, create a Venn diagram like the one included below to compare and contrast the Ottomans and the Safavids.

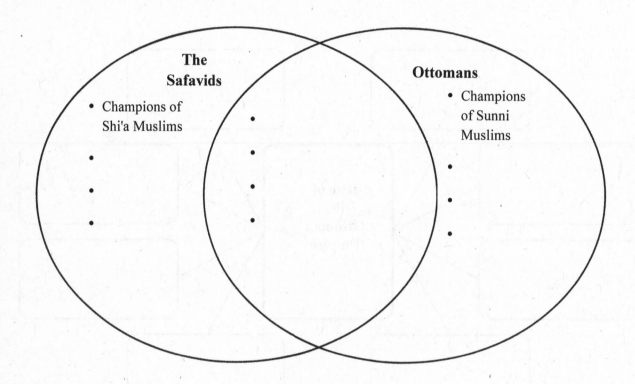

4. THE SHI'A CHALLENGE OF THE SAFAVIDS

As you read this section of your textbook, complete the chart below to note the main ideas about religion and the state in the Safavid Empire.

FOCUS QUESTION: *In the Safavid Empire, what was the relationship between religion and state?*

Religion	State
•	•
•	•
•	•

Using the information in your chart, write a brief answer to the Focus Question.

5. THE MUGHALS AND THE APEX OF MUSLIM CIVILIZATION IN INDIA

As you read this section in your textbook, complete the concept web below to identify main ideas about Akbar's rule of the Mughal Empire.

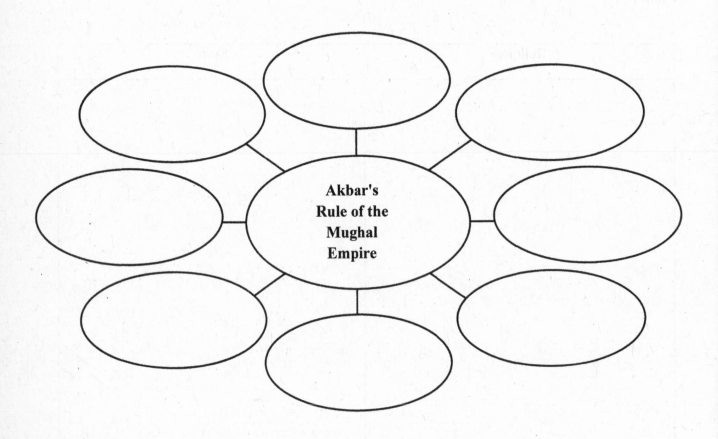

6. THE MUGHALS AND THE APEX OF MUSLIM CIVILIZATION IN INDIA

As you read this section of your textbook, use the table included below to describe key cultural characteristics of the Mughal Empire.

Mughal Culture		
Religion	**Art and Literature**	**Women and Gender**
• Akbar sought to end sectarian division in India		

7. THE MUGHALS AND THE APEX OF MUSLIM CIVILIZATION IN INDIA

After reading this section of your textbook, complete the chart below to compare and contrast gender roles and society in the Ottoman, Safavid, and Mughal Empires.

	Ottoman Empire	Safavid Empire	Mughal Empire
Gender Roles	• • •	• • •	• • •
Society	• • •	• • •	• • •

CHAPTER REVIEW

TERMS, EVENTS, PEOPLE

The following terms, people, and events are important to your understanding of the chapter. Define each one.

Ottoman
Mehmed II
Janissaries
Vizier
Suleymaniye mosque
Safavid dynasty
Sail al-Din
Ismâ'il
Chaldiran
Abbas I, the Great
Imams
Mullahs
Isfahan
Nadir Khan Afshar
Mughal dynasty
Babur
Humayan
Akbar
Din-i-Ilahi
Sati
Taj Mahal
Nur Jahan
Aurangzeb
Marattas

MY KEY TERMS

Write down terms that are unfamiliar. How are the words used? Do other words or examples reveal their meaning? Try to figure out meaning from the context.

SHORT ANSWER REVIEW

Write the word or phrase that best completes each statement or answers the question.

1. By the 1350s, the _____ had advanced from their strongholds in Asia Minor across the Bosporus into Europe.

2. The Ottoman imperial armies were increasingly dominated by troops called _____, men who had been forcibly conscripted as adolescent boys in conquered territories.

3. Day-to-day administration in the Ottoman Empire was carried out by a large bureaucracy headed by a grand _____.

4. Like the Ottomans, the _____ arose from the struggles of rival Turkic groups in the wake of Timurid invasions, but they espoused the Shi'a variant of Islam.

5. Akbar considered his new religion, the _____, which blended elements of many faiths with which he was familiar, as the long-term key to his efforts to reconcile Hindus and Muslims.

6. The Muslim and Hindu warrior aristocracy that formed the core of the supporters of the _____ dynasty were, like their Ottoman and Safavid counterparts, granted villages for their support.

7. Akbar legally prohibited _____, or the immolation of high-caste Hindu women on their husbands' funeral pyres.

8. Although the later Safavid shahs played down claims to divinity that had been set forth under Ismâ'il and his predecessors, they continued to claim descent from one of the Shi'a _____, or successors of Ali.

9. _____, who were both local mosque officials and prayer leaders, were also supervised by and given some support from the Safavid state.

10. The victory of _____ led to the reunification of the Ottoman Empire following the temporary setbacks caused by Timur's invasion.

MULTIPLE CHOICE REVIEW

Choose the one alternative that best completes the statement or answers the question.

1. Which of the following represents a similarity between the three Muslim early modern empires?
a. All were derived from the Ozbeg Turks.
b. All dynasties depended on effective use of firearms and cannon.
c. Each empire was composed of a majority of Muslims.
d. All of the empires created slave regiments who dominated the rulers.

2. Mehmed II of the Ottoman Empire was responsible for
a. enlarging the empire's territories to their greatest extent.
b. driving the Venetians from the eastern Mediterranean
c. the conquest of Constantinople.
d. the dissolution of the Janissaries.

3. What was the principle of succession within the Ottoman Empire?
a. The Ottoman Empire lacked a clear principle of succession.
b. Succession was based on primogeniture.
c. Like the Orthodox Caliphs of early Islam, succession to the sultanate was elective.
d. Ottoman sultans selected their successors prior to their death.

4. Which of the following was a cause for the decline of the Ottoman Empire?
a. The sultans' destruction of the Janissaries left them without an effective military force.
b. The addition of European military technology such as light artillery made the Janissaries so powerful that they could successfully challenge the authority of the sultans.
c. The conquest of Constantinople by the Holy Roman Empire in 1517 led to the rapid collapse of the Ottoman Empire.
d. Oppressive demands of local officials caused the peasantry to abandon their holdings and flee.

5. The Safavid dynasty had its origins in the 14th century in a family devoted to what group of Islamic
mystics?
a. Sunnite
b. Isma'ili
c. Sufi
d. Sikh

6. Which of the following represents a similarity between the Ottomans and the Safavids?
a. Both recruited regiments of slave boys.
b. Each empire extended their territories into eastern Europe.
c. Both empires lacked substantial non-Muslim populations.
d. Both empires had their geographical origins in Anatolia.

7. Which of the following represents a difference between the Safavid and Ottoman economies?
a. Only the Ottomans sought to encourage artisans and handicraft production.
b. The Safavid market economy was more constricted than that of the Ottomans.
c. Only the Safavid rulers patronized public works projects.
d. The Ottomans alone pursued policies to increase internal and international trade.

8. Which of the following statements concerning the status of women in the Islamic heartlands during the early modern period is most accurate?
a. Islamic women generally enjoyed more liberties than they did in the nomadic social system.
b. Women readily accepted the diminution of status that accompanied the creation of the Islamic empires.
c. Many women in the Islamic heartlands struggled against social restrictions in dress and confinement.
d. Women were carefully excluded from trade and money lending.

9. Which of the following was *NOT* one of the social reforms of Akbar?
a. Prostitution was eliminated from his realm.
b. He attempted to eradicate the practice of sati.
c. He encouraged the establishment of special market days for women.
d. He discouraged child marriages.

10. Which of the following statements concerning the economy of the Mughal Empire is most accurate?
a. Unlike the other Muslim empires, the Mughals successfully banned European merchants from their markets.
b. The Mughal Empire produced nothing of value to the West, but served as a conduit of products from Southeast Asia.
c. French, Dutch, and English merchants brought products from throughout Asia to exchange for the subcontinent's famed cotton textiles.
d. The Indian markets of the Mughals were flooded with Western products.

READING REVIEW: MAKING CONNECTIONS

After reading and studying the chapter, review your understanding by answering each of the following questions, which emphasize important ideas within the chapter.

1. How were the three Muslim empires similar? How were they different?

2. What were the causes of the Ottoman decline in the 17th century?

3. How was the Ottoman decline similar to that of the Abbasids? How was it different?

4. Compare and contrast the social and economic organizations of the Ottomans and Safavids.

5. What were the reasons for the failure of the Mughal dynasty?

6. What weaknesses were common to all of the Muslim empires?

CHAPTER 22
Asian Transitions in an Age of Global Change

Complete the following exercises in order *as you read* the chapter.

INTRODUCTION

Chapter introductions are a valuable guide to the material you are about to read, telling you what topics will be covered and how they fit together. If you keep the "big picture" provided by the introduction in mind as you read the chapter, you will find it much easier to organize your notes, identify important information, and avoid getting lost in the details. With this in mind, re-read the introduction to Chapter 22. As you read, make a list of the key topics you expect to learn about.

Key Topics

_____

_____

_____

_____

_____

_____

_____

_____

_____

_____

_____

_____

_____

_____

_____

_____

_____

_____

_____

1. ASIAN TRADING WORLD AND THE COMING OF THE EUROPEANS

As you read this section in your textbook, take notes on the efforts of the Portuguese, English, and Dutch to take control of the Asian trading world in the table below.

European Expansion in Asia		
Portugal	**England**	**The Netherlands**
• The Portuguese sought to overturn the traditional rules of Asian trade. • •	• • •	• • •

2. MING CHINA: A GLOBAL MISSION REFUSED

As you read this section in your textbook, complete the following outline to describe Ming domestic and foreign policies.

I. Another Scholar-Gentry Revival

    A. The Scholar-Gentry and the Hongwu Emperor

3. MING CHINA: A GLOBAL MISSION REFUSED

As you read this section in your textbook, complete the chart below to summarize key aspects contributing to the economic growth in the early Ming period.

Economic Growth of the Early Ming Period			
Agriculture	**Population**	**Commerce**	**Arts**
•	•	•	•
•	•	•	•
•	•	•	•

4. FENDING OFF THE WEST: JAPAN'S REUNIFICATION AND THE FIRST CHALLENGE

As you read this section of your textbook, complete the flow chart below to trace the internal development of the Japanese state in the early modern period, as well as the impact on Japan's development of the arrival of Europeans.

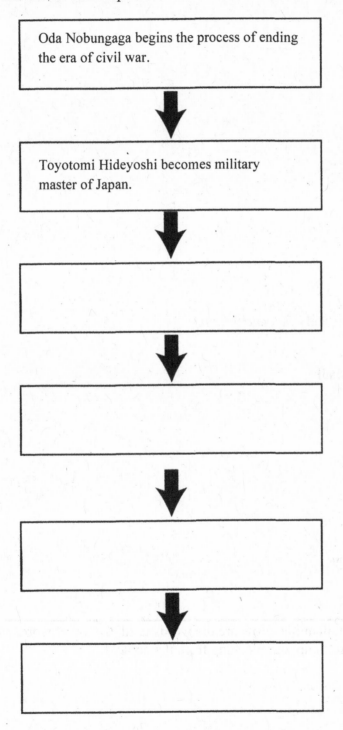

Oda Nobungaga begins the process of ending the era of civil war.

Toyotomi Hideyoshi becomes military master of Japan.

TERMS, EVENTS, PEOPLE

The following terms, people, and events are important to your understanding of the chapter. Define each one.

Asian sea trading network

Goa

Ormuz

Malacca

Batavia

Luzon

Mindanao

Francis Xavier

Robert di Nobili

Hongwu

Macao and Canton

The Water Margin, *Monkey*, and *The Golden Lotus*

Zheng He

Matteo Ricci and Adam Schall

Chongzhen

Nobunaga

Toyotomi Hideyoshi

Tokugawa Ieyasu

Edo

Deshima

School of National Learning

MY KEY TERMS

Write down terms that are unfamiliar. How are the words used? Do other words or examples reveal their meaning? Try to figure out meaning from the context.

Write the word or phrase that best completes each statement or answers the question.

1. The Asian sea-trading network consisted of three zones: the Arab zone, selling glass, carpet, and tapestry; India, selling cotton textiles; and _____, exporting paper, porcelain, and silk.

2. Although the Chinese had ships that were larger and in some respects better built, none of the Asian peoples possessed oceangoing vessels that were as swift and maneuverable as the Portuguese _____.

3. The conquest of the northern Philippine island of _____ was facilitated by the fact that the animistic peoples inhabiting it lived in small states the Spanish could subjugate one by one.

4. The repeated failure of Spanish expeditions to conquer the southern Philippine island of _____ was because it was ruled by a single kingdom whose Muslim rulers were determined to resist Christian dominance.

5. In India from the 1540s onward, _____ and his coworkers brought initial Christian conversions in the tens of thousands.

6. Between 1405 and 1423, a Chinese court eunuch named _____ led seven major expeditions overseas.

7. Brilliant Jesuit scholars, such as _____ and Adam Schall, spent most of their time in the Chinese imperial city correcting calendars, forging cannons, fixing clocks, and demonstrating the accuracy of their instruments.

8. The Zhurchens, or _____, from the region to the northeast of the Chinese Empire, not the Mongols, seized power after the fall of the Ming dynasty.

9. The _____ dynasty proved to be the last of a succession of Chinese imperial houses.

10. After the death of Nobunaga, his ablest general, _____, moved quickly to punish the traitors and to renew the drive to break the power of the daimyos.

MULTIPLE CHOICE REVIEW

Choose the one alternative that best completes the statement or answers the question.

1. At what market did the Europeans first discover that they possessed little of value in the markets of the Eastern sea-trading network?
a. Constantinople
b. Canton
c. Calicut
d. Deshima

2. Which of the following statements most accurately reflects the nature of the Asian sea-trading network?
a. Trade within the network was limited to regional exchange.
b. The islands on the periphery of the major empires supplied raw materials to the empires.
c. The island regions of southeast Asia were never incorporated into the commercial system.
d. Manufactured items were not part of the trade network.

3. Lacking trade goods that Asians wanted to buy, what did the Portuguese do to get the spices and other Asian trade goods they wanted?
a. They imported African slaves into India and China in exchange for spices.
b. They seized control of important ports like Ormuz, seeking to control Asian trade networks.
c. They worked as mercenaries and military advisers to the Mughals and the Chinese.
d. They focused on transporting goods for the Ottoman Empire.

4. Despite having captured Malacca, why did the Dutch move their trading headquarters to Batavia?
a. Malacca was captured by the Mughal Empire.
b. Malacca was destroyed during the monsoon season of 1665.
c. Batavia was closer to the sources of spice production.
d. Batavia was the capital of the kingdom of Siam.

5. What Jesuit missionary was responsible for creating the strategy of converting Hindu elites as a means of achieving mass conversions?
a. Francis Xavier
b. Robert Di Nobili
c. Matteo Ricci
d. Adam Schall

6. Which of the following reforms was introduced by the first Ming emperor?
a. The power of the eunuchs was expanded.
b. The status of women was enhanced.
c. The position of the scholar-gentry within the bureaucracy was restored.
d. The civil service examination system was abolished.

7. Among other results, the Spanish and Portuguese conquests in the Americas affected China greatly because
a. new food crops like peanuts and corn brought by the Spanish and Portuguese from the Americas caused China's population to rise.
b. China became a major importer of Brazilian coffee and Mexican cotton.
c. silver and gold from Peru and Brazil destroyed the silver industry in China.
d. crop-destroying insects from the Americas accidentally introduced to China by the Spanish and the Portuguese resulted in several famines.

8. Why did the Chinese abandon the commercial voyages of the Zhenghe expeditions?
a. Many of the ships were lost as a result of poor ship design and inadequate sailing technique.
b. The size of the fleets were limited, so they could not compete with the Europeans.
c. With death of the emperor who sponsored them, political support for the voyages evaporated.
d. The trade with foreign regions produced a negative balance of trade that drained China of its scarce supply of bullion.

9. Which of the following was *NOT* a policy imposed as a result of Japanese isolationism in the 17th century?
a. Christianity was banned and Christians were persecuted.
b. Foreign traders were confined to the island of Deshima in Nagasaki Bay.
c. Neo-Confucian philosophy gave way to the influence of the school of *National Learning*.
d. The Japanese elite abandoned all contact with Western learning and technological advance.

10. Which of the following was responsible for the reestablishment of the shogunate in Japan?
a. Toyotomi Hideyoshi
b. Nobunaga
c. Tokugawa Ieyasu
d. Hiaru Ashikaga

After reading and studying the chapter, review your understanding by answering each of the following questions, which emphasize important ideas within the chapter.

1. What was the nature of the Asian sea-trading network prior to the arrival of the Portuguese?

2. What did the Portuguese discover at Calicut? How did they respond?

3. How were the Dutch able to displace the Portuguese? How did their participation in the Asian trading network differ from their Portuguese predecessors?

4. Where did the Europeans establish tribute systems?

5. How successful were European missionary efforts by the early 1600s?

6. How did the Ming restore the traditional Chinese forms of government?

7. Why did the Chinese withdraw from commercial expansion?

8. What steps led to the restoration of the Japanese shogunate?

9. Why did the Japanese resort to isolation in the face of European expansion?

CHAPTER 23
The Emergence of Industrial Society in the West, 1750–1914

Complete the following exercises in order *as you read* the chapter.

INTRODUCTION

Chapter introductions are a valuable guide to the material you are about to read, telling you what topics will be covered and how they fit together. If you keep the "big picture" provided by the introduction in mind as you read the chapter, you will find it much easier to organize your notes, identify important information, and avoid getting lost in the details. With this in mind, re-read the introduction to Chapter 23. As you read, make a list of the key topics you expect to learn about.

Key Topics

_____

_____

_____

_____

_____

_____

_____

_____

_____

_____

_____

_____

_____

_____

_____

_____

_____

_____

_____

_____

1. THE AGE OF REVOLUTION

As you read this section in your textbook, complete the following outline to describe the revolutions that shook the Western world between 1776 and 1848.

I. Forces of Change in Europe

      A. The Enlightenment

2. THE AGE OF REVOLUTION

As you read this section of your textbook, complete the list to summarize the lasting reforms of the French Revolution.

Reforms of the French Revolution

1.

2.

3.

4.

---

3. THE CONSOLIDATION OF THE INDUSTRIAL ORDER, 1850-1914

As you read this section in your textbook, take notes on the major European economic, political, and social developments in the second half of the nineteenth century in the table below.

Consolidation of the Industrial Order		
City Life and Factory Work	**The Politics of Nationalism**	**Society and Government**
• Population growth rates stabilized in the second half of the nineteenth century.		

4. CULTURAL TRANSFORMATIONS

As you read this section in your textbook, complete the concept web included below to identify cultural trends in late nineteenth-century Europe.

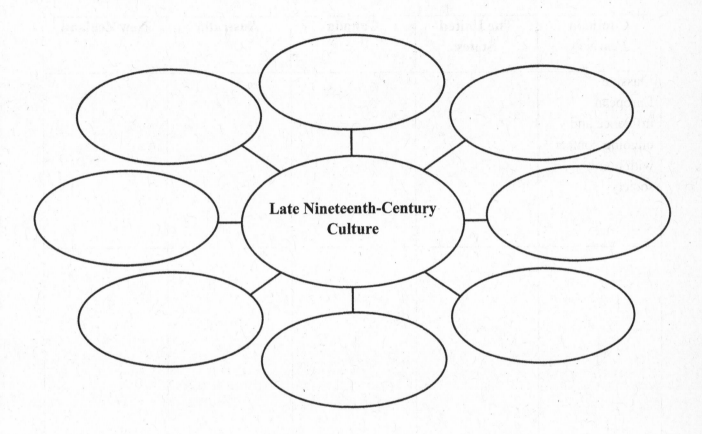

5. WESTERN SETTLER SOCIETIES

As you read this section in your textbook, take notes on the emergence of settler societies in the United States, Australia, Canada, and New Zealand in the table below. Use the first column to list features common to all four societies.

Common Features	The United States	Canada	Australia	New Zealand
Massive European influence and ongoing contact with home society				

6. DIPLOMATIC TENSIONS AND WORLD WAR I

As you read this section in your textbook, complete the following outline to describe the diplomatic tensions in the decades leading up to World War I.

I. The New Alliance System

      A. The Triple Alliance and the Triple Entente

TERMS, EVENTS, PEOPLE

The following terms, people, and events are important to your understanding of the chapter. Define each one.

Population revolution

Proto-industrialization

American Revolution

French Revolution

Louis XVI

Declaration of the Rights of Man and the Citizen

Guillotine

Maximilien Robespierre

Napoleon Bonaparte

Congress of Vienna

Liberalism

Radicals

Socialism

Nationalism

Greek Revolution

French Revolution of 1830

Belgian Revolution of 1830

Reform Bill of 1832

James Watt

Factory system

French Revolution of 1848

Revolutions of 1848

Louis Pasteur

Benjamin Disraeli

Camillo di Cavour

Otto von Bismarck

American Civil War (1861–1865)

Social question

Karl Marx

Revisionism

Feminist movements

Mass leisure culture

Charles Darwin

Albert Einstein

Sigmund Freud

Romanticism

American exceptionalism

Triple Alliance

Triple Entente

Balkan nationalism

MY KEY TERMS

Write down terms that are unfamiliar. How are the words used? Do other words or examples reveal their meaning? Try to figure out meaning from the context.

Write the word or phrase that best completes each statement or answers the question.

1. It was the _____ that most clearly set in motion the political restructuring of western Europe.

2. Thousands of people were executed during the _____, the radical phase of the French Revolution.

3. The final phase of the French Revolution was ushered in by the victory of _____, a leading general who soon converted the republic to an authoritarian empire.

4. _____ focused primarily on issues of political structure, as they sought ways to limit state interference in individual life.

5. _____ wanted wider voting rights and, in some cases, outright democracy.

6. The essence of the _____ was technological change, particularly the application of engines driven by coal to the production process.

7. Count _____ in the Italian state of Piedmont began to support industrial development and extend the powers of parliament to please liberal forces.

8. _____ held that emotion and impression, not reason and generalization, were the keys to the mysteries of human experience and nature itself.

9. Germany, Austria-Hungary, and Italy formed the _____.

10. Britain, Russia, and France constituted the _____.

Choose the one alternative that best completes the statement or answers the question.

1. Proto-industrialization refers to
a. the strictly agricultural economy that preceded the Industrial Revolution.
b. the development of the factory system.
c. the employment of laborers who worked at home but in a capitalist system dependent on urban merchants.
d. the development of systems of transportation necessary for full industrialization.

2. Which of the following was a cause of the French Revolution?
a. Enlightenment endorsement of absolute monarchy
b. middle-class demand for a greater political role
c. continued influence of the Protestant clergy at the French court
d. French territorial additions during the French and Indian Wars

3. Which of the following is *NOT* a characteristic of 19th century liberals?
a. They urged economic reforms that would promote industrialization.
b. They sought to gain representation for people with property in government.
c. They wanted to limit the role of government in individual lives.
d. They urged the importance of national unity and glory.

4. Which of the following statements concerning the revolutions of 1848 is most accurate?
a. Nationalist agitation failed as the armies of Prussia and Austria-Hungary restored the political status quo.
b. In France, the concept of monarchy and authoritarian government was irrevocably overthrown.
c. The map of central Europe was dramatically revised as new nations arose in Germany and Italy.
d. Although nationalist rebellions failed in 1848, the working classes gained permanent advantages never to be lost.

5. Which of the following statements concerning the general prosperity of Europeans by 1900 is most accurate?
a. Despite the technological successes of the Industrial Revolution, the living standards for most Europeans had declined.
b. The working classes remained almost without exception in abject poverty.
c. The Industrial Revolution reduced class distinctions so that almost all Europeans were better off.
d. By 1900, nearly two-thirds of the European population lived above subsistence level.

6. As industrialization spread, peasants in Europe improved their condition by undertaking all of the following *EXCEPT*:
a. joining trades unions.
b. forming cooperatives.
c. specializing in new cash crops.
d. seeking education and new technical skills.

7. Karl Marx argued that the prime force shaping human history was/were
a. developments in the nature of family life.
b. the rise and fall of centralizing empires.
c. the available means of production and who controlled those means.
d. the spread of the great world religions, including Christianity and Islam.

8. Around 1900, the most important supporters of feminist movements were
a. lower-class women seeking better working conditions.
b. Protestant clergy in the United States, as part of the temperance campaign.
c. middle-class women who believed they could be a moral voice in politics.
d. European nationalists, who saw improvements for women to be essential for national growth.

9. The artistic movement known as romanticism was characterized by
a. a general distaste for nature.
b. a well developed synthesis between rationality, technology, and human emotion.
c. a belief that emotion and impression were key in understanding human experience.
d. a rigid formalism in painting, sculpture, and literature.

10. How did the development of Australia, New Zealand, and Canada differ from that of the United States?
a. They received little of the large wave of migrants who left Europe in the 19th century.
b. They were unable to gain control of native inhabitants until after the 19th century.
c. They failed to develop parliamentary governments until early in the 20th century.
d. Limited industrialization and continued political ties to Britain left them much more dependent on Europe.

READING REVIEW: MAKING CONNECTIONS

After reading and studying the chapter, review your understanding by answering each of the following questions, which emphasize important ideas within the chapter.

1. What were the causes of the American Revolution? The French Revolution?

2. What new political movements emerged in the aftermath of the French Revolution?

3. What changes in social organization did industrialization cause?

4. How were industrialization and revolution linked?

5. How did government functions increase in response to the "social question"?

6. How did science and the arts diverge in the period after 1850?

7. How did industrialization lead to an expansion of the West's influence in the world?

Industrialization and Imperialism: The Making of the European Global Order

Complete the following exercises in order *as you read* the chapter.

INTRODUCTION

Chapter introductions are a valuable guide to the material you are about to read, telling you what topics will be covered and how they fit together. If you keep the "big picture" provided by the introduction in mind as you read the chapter, you will find it much easier to organize your notes, identify important information, and avoid getting lost in the details. With this in mind, re-read the introduction to Chapter 24. As you read, make a list of the key topics you expect to learn about.

Key Topics

_____

_____

_____

_____

_____

_____

_____

_____

_____

_____

_____

_____

_____

_____

_____

_____

_____

1. THE SHIFT TO LAND EMPIRES IN ASIA

As you read this section in your textbook, take notes on Dutch and British imperialism in Asia in the table below.

	The British in India	The Dutch in Indonesia
Colonial Government		
Colonial Society		
Social Reform		

2. INDUSTRIAL RIVALRIES AND THE PARTITION OF THE WORLD, 1870-1914

As you read this section of your textbook, complete the list below of the key advances in military technology that facilitated Western imperialism. Some items have been completed for you.

Key Advances in Military Technology

1. Advances in metallurgy make mass production of artillery possible

2. Better rifles multiply the firepower of European soldiers

3.

4.

5.

6.

7.

8.

3. PATTERNS OF DOMINANCE: CONTINUITY AND CHANGE

As you read this section in your textbook, complete the following outline to describe the changes in the relationship between colonizers and their subject peoples over the course of the nineteenth century. Some items have been completed for you.

I. Colonial Regimes and Social Hierarchies

    A. Divide and Conquer

CHAPTER REVIEW

TERMS, EVENTS, PEOPLE

The following terms, people, and events are important to your understanding of the chapter. Define each one.

Kingdom of Mataram

Sepoys

Raj

Plassey (1757)

Robert Clive

Presidencies

Princely states

Nabobs

Charles Cornwallis

Isandhlwana (1879)

Tropical dependencies

White Dominions

Settler colonies

White racial supremacy

Great Trek

Boer republics

Cecil Rhodes

Boer War (1899–1902)

James Cook

Kamehameha

MY KEY TERMS

Write down terms that are unfamiliar. How are the words used? Do other words or examples reveal their meaning? Try to figure out meaning from the context.

Write the word or phrase that best completes each statement or answers the question.

1. The rise of the British _____ in India owed much to the rivalry between the British and the French.

2. Madras, Bombay, and Calcutta became the administrative centers of the three _____ that made up the bulk of the territory that Britain ruled in India.

3. The venality and misgovernment of the Indian _____ resulted in the catastrophic Bengal famine of 1770.

4. A succession of reforms in India culminated in sweeping measures taken in the 1790s by Lord _____.

5. The greater portion of European empires consisted of _____ in Africa, Asia, and the South Pacific in which small numbers of Europeans ruled large numbers of non-Western peoples.

6. In _____, the descendants of European settlers made up the overwhelming majority of the population.

7. In _____ colonies, Europeans and indigenous peoples increasingly clashed over land rights, resource control, social status, and differences in culture.

8. When diamonds were discovered in the Orange Free State in 1867, British entrepreneurs such as _____ began to move in.

9. Hawaii was opened to the West through the voyages of Captain _____ from 1777 to 1779.

10. King _____ of Hawaii promoted economic change, encouraging Western merchants to establish export trade in Hawaiian goods in return for increasing revenues to the royal treasury.

Choose the one alternative that best completes the statement or answers the question.

1. European expansionism in the late 19th century was motivated in part by
a. fear of the expanding power of the Ottoman Empire.
b. the need to recover from defeats handed to them by the Qing Dynasty in China.
c. rivalries between European nations, as well as rivalries with Japan and the United States.
d. the need to control markets which would purchase European raw materials.

2. In what way was the intrusion of the British East India Company into India similar to the Dutch entry into Java?
a. the conversion of the Indian elite to Christianity
b. the willingness of Company officials to intervene in conflicts among the indigenous rulers
c. the British removal of all local rulers in the 18th century
d. the direct intervention of the British government in the process

3. Which of the following statements concerning the Indian resistance to British colonialism is most accurate?
a. Following the defeat at Plassey, the Princely States unified to oppose British advance.
b. Following Plassey, there was no resistance to British control of India.
c. The greatest opponent of British colonialism in India was the resurgent Mughal Empire.
d. Indian princes continued to focus on fighting with each other despite the British threat.

4. The early period of Dutch and British rule in India and Java
a. left Javanese and Indian lords with little control over the peasantry.
b. left the indigenous aristocratic class and old ruling families largely preserved.
c. totally disrupted the indigenous social systems of Java and India.
d. led to the creation of large middle classes in India and Java.

5. What was the most critical issue for British reformers considering India in the 1830s?
a. sacred cows
b. multiple marriages
c. infant marriages
d. sati

6. Which of the following statements is most accurate?
a. Faced with advanced military technology, indigenous peoples ceased resisting the imperial advance.
b. Europeans were unable to overcome the Asian advantages in population.
c. African and Asian peoples often fiercely resisted colonial rule, although without realistic chances of permanent success.
d. No African or Asian military forces ever won set battles.

7. From the late 19th century to World War I, relations between Europeans and colonized people
a. were characterized by a high degree of social mixture.
b. were strained because of the growing importance of the idea of white racial superiority.
c. remained largely what they had been over the previous three centuries.
d. were strained because of increasing religiously-motivated violence.

8. Which of the following statements concerning the internal economies of the European colonies is most accurate?
a. The introduction of European technology, such as railways and telegraphs, was intended to improve the internal economies of the colonies.
b. Slowly the industrial system of the West was introduced into Asia and Africa.
c. By 1914, Asian and African colonies had won economic independence from the European colonizers.
d. Colonial economies were steadily reduced to dependence on the European-dominated global market.

9. What was the most serious source of conflict between the Boer and the British in South Africa?
a. the efforts of the British to eradicate slavery in the Boer communities
b. Boer efforts to seize land held by the Zulus and the Xhosa
c. the culture clash between the rural British and more urban Boer
d. British efforts to convert the Boer to Anglicanism

10. The Hawaiian ruler Kamehameha is notable because
a. he resisted the efforts of the British to interfere in Hawaiian politics.
b. he drove out Western merchants, isolating Hawaii from international trade.
c. he unified the Hawaiian island into a single kingdom.
d. his conversion to Christianity began an extensive wave of conversions throughout the islands

After reading and studying the chapter, review your understanding by answering each of the following questions, which emphasize important ideas within the chapter.

1. Contrast the motives for imperialism in the preindustrial era with those of the industrial era.

2. In what way did the Dutch control of Java provide a model for early European industrial advance?

3. Contrast social interaction with indigenous peoples before and after 1850.

4. What were the motives behind the global scramble for colonies?

5. Compare and contrast tropical dependencies, White Dominions, and contested settler colonies.

6. How did the nineteenth-century European imperialists transform their methods of economic extraction?

7. How were European settler colonies established in the 1800s different from those from earlier centuries, and what impact did those differences have?

8. In what ways were the European colonial systems vulnerable?

Complete the following exercises in order *as you read* the chapter.

INTRODUCTION

Chapter introductions are a valuable guide to the material you are about to read, telling you what topics will be covered and how they fit together. If you keep the "big picture" provided by the introduction in mind as you read the chapter, you will find it much easier to organize your notes, identify important information, and avoid getting lost in the details. With this in mind, re-read the introduction to Chapter 25. As you read, make a list of the key topics you expect to learn about.

Key Topics

_____

_____

_____

_____

_____

_____

_____

_____

_____

_____

_____

_____

_____

_____

_____

_____

_____

_____

_____

_____

1. FROM COLONIES TO NATIONS

As you read this section in your textbook, take notes on the Latin American independence movements in the table below. Use the first column to describe external events that contributed to uprisings across Latin America.

External Events	Mexico	Northern South America	Southern South America	Brazil
American Revolution provides model for revolt				

2. New Nations Confront Old and New Problems

As you read this section of your textbook, complete the list below of the most important challenges facing the new nations of Latin America.

Challenges Facing New Nations

1. Ethnic division, oppression, and prejudice

2. Political fragmentation

3.

4.

5.

6.

7.

8.

---

3. LATIN AMERICAN ECONOMICS AND WORLD MARKETS, 1820-1870

As you read this section in your textbook, take notes on economic developments in Mexico, Argentina, and Brazil in the table below.

European Expansion in Asia		
Mexico	**Argentina**	**Brazil**
• Mexican republic established in 1824		

4. SOCIETIES IN SEARCH OF THEMSELVES

As you read this section in your textbook, complete the following outline to describe cultural, social, and economic developments in Latin America in the nineteenth and early twentieth centuries.

I. Cultural Expression After Independence

    A. Romanticism

TERMS, EVENTS, PEOPLE

The following terms, people, and events are important to your understanding of the chapter. Define each one.

Toussaint L'Overture

Miguel de Hidalgo

Augustín de Iturbide

Simon Bolívar

Gran Colombia

José de San Martín

João VI

Pedro I

Andrés Santa Cruz

Caudillos

Centralists

Federalists

Monroe Doctrine

Guano

Positivism

Antonio López de Santa Anna

Manifest Destiny

Mexican-American War

Treaty of Guadalupe-Hidalgo (1848)

Benito Juárez

La Reforma

Maximilian von Habsburg

Gauchos

Juan Manuel de Rosas

Argentine Republic

Domingo F. Sarmiento

Fazendas

Modernization theory

Dependency theory

Porfirio Díaz

Cientificos

Spanish-American War

Panama Canal

My Key Terms

Write down terms that are unfamiliar. How are the words used? Do other words or examples reveal their meaning? Try to figure out meaning from the context.

Write the word or phrase that best completes each statement or answers the question.

1. Under the able leadership of _____ and other blacks, the independent republic of Haiti was proclaimed in 1804.

2. In 1808, Napoleon placed the king of Spain and his son under arrest and forced them to abdicate in favor of his _____.

3. In northern South America, _____, a wealthy Creole officer, emerged as the leader of the revolt against Spain.

4. A struggle often developed between _____, who wanted to create strong national governments with broad powers, and federalists, who wanted policies to be set by regional governments.

5. The _____ of 1823 stated clearly that any attempt to colonize in the Americas would be considered an unfriendly act by the United States.

6. Following defeat in the Mexican American War, Mexico was forced to sign the disadvantageous Treaty of _____.

7. At French urging, _____, an Austrian archduke, was convinced to take the throne of Mexico in 1862.

8. The United Provinces of the Rio de la Plata, which declared their independence in 1816, soon split apart, and local caudillos, able to call on the support of mounted rural workers, or _____, dominated each region.

9. By 1862, in a movement resembling La Reforma in Mexico, the provinces surrounding the Rio de la Plata were united in a unified nation called the _____.

10. In the provinces of Rio de Janeiro and Sao Paulo, coffee estates, or _____, began to spread toward the interior as new lands were opened.

Choose the one alternative that best completes the statement or answers the question.

1. Which of these was *NOT* a problem that faced the leaders of newly independent Latin American nations?
a. Their colonial heritage left little legacy of participatory government.
b. They had no economic relations with Europe or the United States.
c. Their colonial heritage left their citizens both dependent on and resentful of central authority.
d. They found themselves in weak or dependent economic relations with industrialized Europe.

2. Who was the leader of the independence movement in northern South America?
a. Father Miguel de Hidalgo
b. Bernardino Rivadavia
c. Simon Bolívar
d. José de San Martín

3. How was the experience of the Napoleonic Wars different for Portugal than for Spain?
a. Portugal was allied with the French emperor.
b. The French attempted to invade Portugal but failed.
c. The entire royal family of Portugal fled to Brazil and set up their capital there.
d. Following the defeat of the Portuguese, the French took over the colonial administration of Brazil.

4. Which of these was *NOT* a factor that caused most attempts at consolidation and union to fail in early 19th century Latin America?
a. Most of Latin America was divided into units that mirrored the colonial viceroyalties.
b. Enormous geographic barriers separated nations from each other and divided them internally.
c. Road systems were poor and transportation rudimentary.
d. Latin America was deeply divided along religious lines.

5. Which of the following concepts was associated with Latin American liberal groups?
a. retention of corporate groups
b. the defense of the Catholic Church
c. the rights of individuals and belief in a secular society
d. intervention by the state in commerce through protective tariffs

6. Which of the following factors was *NOT* a feature of economic growth in Latin America after 1850?
a. rapid industrialization
b. the growth of cities, providing good internal markets
c. European demand for Latin American products
d. improvements in transportation

7. Liberalism in late 19th century Latin America included a belief in positivism, which stressed
a. the importance of mass democracy.
b. the dependency model of economic development.
c. the importance of class conflict in shaping history.
d. observation and a scientific approach to the problems of society.

8. Latin American writers and artists in the 1830's
a. took part in a neoclassical revival.
b. emphasized the importance exotic and distinctive aspects of American society.
c. rejected the American Indian roots of their cultures.
d. depended completely on Europe for inspiration.

9. Which of the following beliefs is *NOT* associated with the concept of "modernization" or "westernization?"
a. Development was a matter of increasing per capita production in any society.
b. The more industrialized and urbanized any society became, the more social change and improvement were possible as traditional patterns were transformed.
c. Change would take place through radical or revolutionary transitions rather than gradually.
d. As the process occurred, there would be a natural movement toward more democratic forms of government and popular participation.

10. Which of the following sectors of the Latin American economy fueled the boom of the post-1880 period?
a. industrial production
b. the export of raw materials
c. the internal marketing of raw materials
d. the internal capitalization of transportation networks

READING REVIEW: MAKING CONNECTIONS

After reading and studying the chapter, review your understanding by answering each of the following questions, which emphasize important ideas within the chapter.

1. What were the causes of political change in Latin America?

2. Contrast Brazilian independence with other independence movements in Latin America.

3. What was the federalist vs. centralist controversy? How were political parties involved?

4. Characterize the liberal politics of the period from 1850 to 1870. Who were the major liberal politicians in Latin American countries?

5. How successful was reform at resolving the problems of race, class, and gender?

6. What was the nature of the economic boom during the period after 1870? What were the potential drawbacks of the boom?

7. In what way did the United States enter the political and economic affairs of Latin America?

CHAPTER 26
Civilizations in Crisis: The Ottoman Empire, the Islamic Heartlands, and Qing China

Complete the following exercises in order *as you read* the chapter.

INTRODUCTION

Chapter introductions are a valuable guide to the material you are about to read, telling you what topics will be covered and how they fit together. If you keep the "big picture" provided by the introduction in mind as you read the chapter, you will find it much easier to organize your notes, identify important information, and avoid getting lost in the details. With this in mind, re-read the introduction to Chapter 26. As you read, make a list of the key topics you expect to learn about.

Key Topics

_____

_____

_____

_____

_____

_____

_____

_____

_____

_____

_____

_____

_____

_____

_____

1. FROM EMPIRE TO NATION: OTTOMAN RETREAT AND THE BIRTH OF TURKEY

As you read this section in your textbook, trace the course of Ottoman history from crisis, to reform, revolt in the table below.

The Ottoman Empire in Crisis		
Crisis	Reform	Revolt
• A series of weak rulers contributed to Ottoman decline		

2. WESTERN INTRUSIONS AND THE CRISIS IN THE ARAB ISLAMIC HEARTLANDS

As you read this section in your textbook, create a timeline of nineteenth-century Egyptian history.

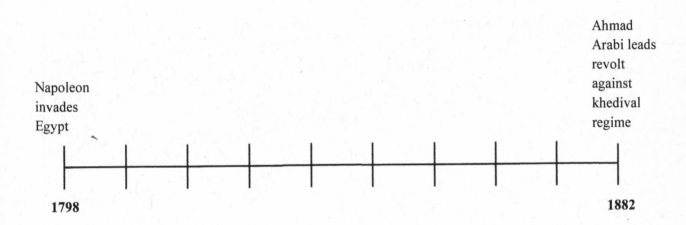

3. THE LAST DYNASTY: THE RISE AND FALL OF THE QING EMPIRE IN CHINA

As you read this section in your textbook, complete the following outline to describe the rise and fall of the Qing Empire.

I. The Fall of the Ming

      A. The Manchu Take Control

CHAPTER REVIEW

TERMS, EVENTS, PEOPLE

The following terms, people, and events are important to your understanding of the chapter. Define each one.

Selim III

Mahmud II

Tanzimat reforms

Abdul Hamid

Ottoman Society for Union and Progress

Mamluks

Murad

Muhammad Ali

Khedives

Suez Canal

Al-Afghani and Muhammad Abduh

Ahmad Orabi

Mahdi

Khalifa Abdallahi

Nurhaci

Banner armies

Kangxi

Compradors

Lin Zexu

Opium War

Taiping Rebellion

Cixi

Boxer Rebelliom

Sun Yat-sen

Puyi

MY KEY TERMS

Write down terms that are unfamiliar. How are the words used? Do other words or examples reveal their meaning? Try to figure out meaning from the context.

Write the word or phrase that best completes each statement or answers the question.

1. The _____ reforms in the Ottoman Empire, between 1839 and 1876 reorganized education, established railways and telegraph systems, and resulted in a constitution based on European prototypes.

2. _____, the head of the coalition of Mamluk households that shared power in Egypt at the time of Napoleon's arrival, dismissed the invader as insignificant.

3. Intermarrying with Turkish families, Muhammad Ali's descendants provided a succession of rulers in Egypt known as _____.

4. The completion of the _____ Canal in 1869 shortened the distance by sea between Europe and Asia and allowed steamboats to replace sailing vessels.

5. At the battle of _____ in 1898, the bulk of the Mahdist cavalry and its commander were slaughtered.

6. Overseas trading links gave rise to a wealthy new group of merchants, the _____, who specialized in the import-export trade on China's southern coast.

7. In the late 1830s, the Chinese emperor sent one of his most distinguished officials, _____, to stamp out the opium trade.

8. Led by a mentally unstable, semi-Christian prophet named Hong Xiuquan, the _____ Rebellion exacerbated stresses within Chinese society.

9. The last decades of the Manchu dynasty were dominated by the ultraconservative dowager empress _____.

10. In 1912, the last of emperor of China, a small boy named _____, was deposed.

MULTIPLE CHOICE REVIEW

Choose the one alternative that best completes the statement or answers the question.

1. The Chinese and Ottoman Empires avoided formal colonization by Europeans in the 19th century because
a. they maintained technological parity with Europe.
b. they developed diplomatic and military alliances which kept the Europeans at bay.
c. they were too large, complex, and militarily powerful to be conquered.
d. they underwent extensive reforms that enabled them to organize resistance to European encroachment.

2. Which of the following European powers seized territories of the Ottoman Empire in the early decades of the 18th century?
a. Austria Hapsburg dynasty
b. Britain
c. France
d. Italy

3. The Ottoman Sultan Mahmud II
a. attempted to rid the Ottoman Empire of Western influences.
b. successfully eliminated the Janissary corps.
c. attempted to restore absolutism and destroy the Western-style constitution of the Turks.
d. was toppled from the throne by a Janissary rebellion.

4. The government of Ottoman Sultan Abdul Hamid
a. pursued an aggressive policy of economic and political liberalization.
b. combined despotic absolutism with a policy of limited westernization.
c. allied itself with young reformist officers in the military.
d. upheld the reforms of the 1878 constitution.

5. By 1801, what ruler had succeeded in establishing his dominance over Egypt?
a. Murad, commander of the Mamluks
b. Napoleon, the French emperor
c. Muhammad Ali, an Albanian officer in the Ottoman army
d. Nurhaci, the Almoravid military commander

6. Ahmad Orabi was
a. a Turkish commander in the Ottoman army that conquered Egypt.
b. the Egyptian army officer who led a revolt against the khedival government in 1882.
c. the Sufi mystic who claimed to be a direct descendant of the Prophet.
d. the Khedive responsible for the construction of the Suez Canal.

7. Which of the following statements concerning the Manchu government is most accurate?
a. It destroyed the scholar-gentry in order to consolidate its grip on the government.
b. The civil service examination system was eliminated as a means of entering the government.
c. Though Manchus occupied a disproportionate number of the highest political positions, there were few limits on high Chinese could rise within the imperial bureaucracy.
d. Chinese officials were eliminated at the local administrative levels in order to prevent the extreme regionalization that had led to the downfall of previous dynasties.

8. Which of the following was *NOT* a feature of the decline of the Qing Dynasty?
a. blatant cheating in the civil service exam system.
b. a sharp decline in the funds available for military spending.
c. the neglect of critical public works, such as dams and dikes.
d. the gradual disappearance of a Chinese merchant class in the face of European competition.

9. What was the impact of the British opium trade on China?
a. Its use was restricted to the peasantry of northern China, where production of food rapidly decreased.
b. The government was quickly able to halt the importation of opium so that it did not have the disastrous impact on the Chinese population that was anticipated.
c. Within years, China's favorable balance of trade was reversed and silver began to flow out of the country.
d. Due to the addiction of the imperial court, the British were welcomed as a valuable trade partner of China.

10. Which of the following rebellions was clandestinely supported by the Qing imperial court under Cixi?
a. the Boxer rebellion
b. the Taiping rebellion
c. the Shandong rebellion
d. the Kangxi rebellion

READING REVIEW: MAKING CONNECTIONS

After reading and studying the chapter, review your understanding by answering each of the following questions, which emphasize important ideas within the chapter.

1. What was the nature of the eighteenth-century crisis in the Ottoman Empire? Why was it not fatal?

2. What reforms were introduced in the Ottoman Empire between the reign of Mahmud II and 1876?

3. What led to the overthrow of the Ottoman Sultanate in 1908?

4. How did Muhammad Ali come to power? What reforms did he introduce?

5. How did the British gain control of Egypt?

6. What reforms did the Manchus introduce? How successful were they?

7. What problems did the Manchu dynasty encounter in the 19th century?

8. How did Europeans gain entry into China?

9. What led to the overthrow of the Manchu dynasty?

CHAPTER 27
Russia and Japan: Industrialization Outside the West

Complete the following exercises in order *as you read* the chapter.

INTRODUCTION

Chapter introductions are a valuable guide to the material you are about to read, telling you what topics will be covered and how they fit together. If you keep the "big picture" provided by the introduction in mind as you read the chapter, you will find it much easier to organize your notes, identify important information, and avoid getting lost in the details. With this in mind, re-read the introduction to Chapter 27. As you read, make a list of the key topics you expect to learn about.

Key Topics

_____

_____

_____

_____

_____

_____

_____

_____

_____

_____

_____

_____

_____

_____

_____

_____

_____

_____

_____

_____

_____

1. RUSSIA'S REFORMS AND INDUSTRIAL ADVANCE

As you read this section in your textbook, complete the table below to make connections between conditions in Russia in the aftermath of the Napoleonic Wars and the policies and initiatives its rulers advanced in the second half of the nineteenth century.

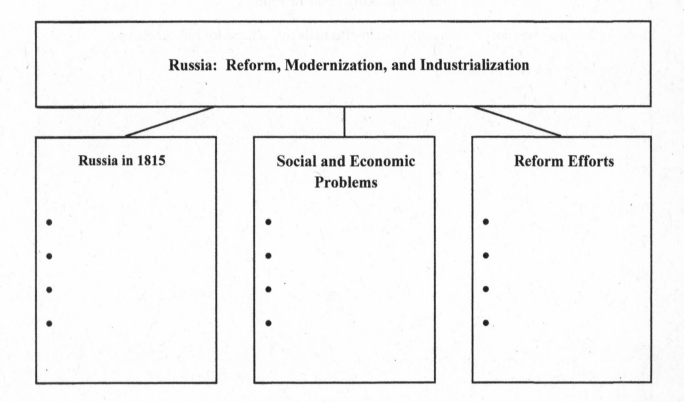

2. PROTEST AND REVOLUTION IN RUSSIA

As you read this section of your textbook, complete the list below of the developments prior to 1905 that pushed Russia towards revolution.

Developments Prior to 1905

1. Many business people, professionals, and intellectuals saw a need for radical change

2. Anarchism took root in Russia

3.

4.

5.

6.

7.

8.

3. JAPAN: TRANSFORMATION WITHOUT REVOLUTION

As you read this section of your textbook, complete the flow chart below to trace the causes and consequences of the fall of the Shogunate and the rise of Meiji state in Japan.

Internal and External Challenges to the Shogunate	Political and Economic Transformation	The Price of Change
• Fiscal problems undermined the Shogunate		

CHAPTER REVIEW

TERMS, EVENTS, PEOPLE

The following terms, people, and events are important to your understanding of the chapter. Define each one.

Holy Alliance

Decembrist rising

Crimean War (1854–1856)

Emancipation of the serfs

Zemstvoes

Trans-Siberian railroad

Count Witte

Intelligentsia

Anarchists

Russo-Japanese War

Lenin (Vladimir Ilych Ulyanov)

Bolsheviks

Russian Revolution of 1905

Duma

Stolypin reforms

Kulaks

Terakoya

Dutch Studies

Matthew Perry

Meiji Restoration

Diet

Zaibatsu

Sino-Japanese War (1894–1895)

Yellow peril

MY KEY TERMS

Write down terms that are unfamiliar. How are the words used? Do other words or examples reveal their meaning? Try to figure out meaning from the context.

Write the word or phrase that best completes each statement or answers the question.

1. Nicholas I provoked conflict with the Ottoman Empire in 1853 with the _____ War.

2. In some ways, the Russian _____ of the serfs in 1861 was more generous than the liberation of the slaves in America.

3. The establishment of the _____ railroad, which connected European Russia with the Pacific, was the crowning achievement of the drive to improve communications.

4. War broke out between Russia and _____ in 1904, leading to a disastrous Russian defeat.

5. Unexpected defeat in war unleashed massive protests on the Russian home front in the _____.

6. Russian liberals were wooed through the creation of national parliament, the _____.

7. A minority of Russian agricultural entrepreneurs called _____ began to increase agricultural production and buy up additional land.

8. The Japanese constitution of 1889 assured major powers for the emperor, along with a parliament, or _____.

9. By the 1890s, huge new industrial combines called _____ were being formed in Japan.

10. Japan's quick victory over _____ in the quarrel for influence over Korea in 1894-1895 marked the first step in colonial expansion.

MULTIPLE CHOICE REVIEW

Choose the one alternative that best completes the statement or answers the question.

1. Which of the following was *NOT* a common feature of industrialization in Japan and Russia?
a. Industrialization fostered social cohesion in both countries.
b. Both countries had a history of adopting profitable learning from other societies.
c. Both entered the industrial age with more effective governments than they had had in the past.
d. Each country used the state to promote changes that were handled in part by private businesses in the West.

2. Which of the following statements concerning Russia's territorial expansion is *NOT* accurate?
a. Russia continued to press for territorial acquisitions in the Ottoman Empire.
b. No massive acquisitions marked the early 19th century.
c. Russia supported nationalist movements in the Balkans.
d. Russia supported nationalist movements in Poland to create a buffer zone between Russia and the West.

3. Which of the following was a feature of the emancipation of the serfs in Russia?
a. Emancipation was designed to retain the tight grips of the tsarist state.
b. Industrialists who depended on the serfs for cheap labor fought emancipation.
c. Emancipation destroyed the power of the traditional aristocracy.
d. Widespread peasant uprisings forced the emancipation of the serfs.

4. One of the important results of the establishment of railway systems in Russia was the opening of
a. the Ukraine.
b. Poland.
c. Siberia.
d. the Crimea.

5. The Russian Revolution of 1905
a. ushered in a democratic era that lasted until World War I.
b. achieved little permanent change because Tsar Nicholas II insisted on autocratic rule.
c. collapsed because the Duma was quickly taken over by radical socialists.
d. collapsed after Russia's defeat in the Russo-Japanese War.

6. Terrorism was the chief political method used by which of the following groups?
a. the old believers
b. anarchists
c. liberals
d. Turgenevs

7. Which of the following statements concerning the Tokugawa shogunate in the 19th century is most accurate?
a. The shogunate bureaucracy had been opened to talented commoners.
b. By the 19th century, the Tokugawa were able to dispense with the feudal organization of earlier Japan.
c. Increasingly, the shogunate depended on its long-standing alliances with Western powers to maintain its dominance.
d. The shogunate continued to combine a central bureaucracy with semifeudal alliances of regional daimyos and the samurai.

8. The Meiji government in Japan
a. like the Russian Revolution of 1905, failed to accomplish long-term reforms.
b. abolished feudalism and centralized political power.
c. combined domestic development with a foreign policy that antagonized the West.
d. failed to either destroy the samurai or to incorporate them into the new economy and political system.

9. One of the major similarities between Japanese and Russian industrialization was the fact that
a. both lacked natural resources.
b. scarce capital and technological inferiority compelled state direction.
c. neither was able to complete construction of a railway system.
d. neither had any experience of cultural exchange with the West.

10. Which of the following was not an effect of industrialization in Japan?
a. steady population growth
b. universal education
c. the rejection of traditional values
d. a shift in Japanese foreign policy

READING REVIEW: MAKING CONNECTIONS

After reading and studying the chapter, review your understanding by answering each of the following questions, which emphasize important ideas within the chapter.

1. Compare and contrast Japan and Russia during the period of industrialization.

2. Describe Russian reform and industrialization from 1861 to 1900.

3. What were the forces leading to the revolution in Russia by 1905?

4. Describe Japanese reform and industrialization from 1853 to 1900.

5. What social and economic changes took place in Japan as a result of industrialization?

6. How do the authors define the nature of the world economic and political system by 1914?

CHAPTER 28
Descent into the Abyss: World War I and the Crisis of the European Global Order

Complete the following exercises in order *as you read* the chapter.

INTRODUCTION

Chapter introductions are a valuable guide to the material you are about to read, telling you what topics will be covered and how they fit together. If you keep the "big picture" provided by the introduction in mind as you read the chapter, you will find it much easier to organize your notes, identify important information, and avoid getting lost in the details. With this in mind, re-read the introduction to Chapter 28. As you read, make a list of the key topics you expect to learn about.

Key Topics

_____

_____

_____

_____

_____

_____

_____

_____

_____

_____

_____

_____

_____

_____

_____

_____

_____

_____

1. THE COMING OF THE GREAT WAR

As you read this section of your textbook, complete the list below of the events and developments that contributed to the outbreak of World War I in 1914.

<table>
<tr><td>

Outbreak of World War I

1. Fear of Germany drove Russia into alliances with France and Britain

2. Germany, Austria, and Italy formed a counter alliance

3.

4.

5.

6.

7.

8.

</td></tr>
</table>

2. A WORLD AT WAR

As you read this section in your textbook, complete the following outline to trace the course of World War I.

I. Stalemate on the Western Front

      A. The Initial German Offensives

3. FAILED PEACE AND GLOBAL TURMOIL

As you read this section in your textbook, complete the table below to compare and contrast the objectives of three key leaders at the Paris peace conference: Georges Clemenceau, David Lloyd George, and Woodrow Wilson.

Georges Clemenceau (France)	David Lloyd George (Britain)	Woodrow Wilson (U.S.)
Intent on punishing Germany		

4. THE NATIONALIST ASSAULT ON THE EUROPEAN COLONIAL ORDER

As you read this section of your textbook, complete the table below to compare and contrast nationalist movements in India and Egypt.

Challenges to Colonial Rule in India and Egypt	
India	**Egypt**
• The National Congress Party grew out of associations of Western-educated Indians.	

CHAPTER REVIEW

TERMS, EVENTS, PEOPLE

The following terms, people, and events are important to your understanding of the chapter. Define each one.

Archduke Ferdinand

Western Front

Eastern Front
Nicholas II
Gallipoli

Italian Front

Armenian genocide

Submarine warfare

Armistice

Georges Clemenceau

David Lloyd George

Woodrow Wilson

Treaty of Versailles

League of Nations

Indian National Congress

B.G. Tilak

Morley-Minto Reforms (1909)

Montagu-Chelmsford reforms (1919)

Rowlatt Act (1919)

M.K. Gandhi

Satyagraha

Lord Cromer

Mustafa Kemal, Ataturk

Effendi

Dinshawi incident

Hussein

Mandates

Balfour Declaration (1917)

Zionism

Leon Pinsker

Theodor Hertzl

Alfred Dreyfus

Wafd Party

W.E.B. Du Bois and Marcus Garvey

Négritude

Léopold S. Senghor, Aimé Césaire, and Léon Damas

My Key Terms

Write down terms that are unfamiliar. How are the words used? Do other words or examples reveal their meaning? Try to figure out meaning from the context.

SHORT ANSWER REVIEW

Write the word or phrase that best completes each statement or answers the question.

1. Russia signed the Treaty of _____ in March 1918, giving Germany substantial territories in western Russia in return for peace.

2. The _____, established after World War I, proved to be little more than a discussion group, as real diplomacy continued on a nation-to-nation basis.

3. The literary movement in France in the early 20th century, called _____, promoted African nationalism.

4. Educated Indian women identified with the heroine in Tagore's _____, a book about the complexity of women's lives in colonial India.

5. Germany issued Austria-Hungary a(n) _____ in its dealings with Serbia after the assassination of Archduke Ferdinand in 1914.

6. Defensive fortifications that ran along the Western Front were commonly called _____, featuring an abysmal existence alongside death, rats, and disease.

7. Before World War I, England, France, and Russia formed the _____, a military alliance in competition with Germany, Austria-Hungary, and Italy.

8. President Woodrow Wilson convinced all sides to sign a(n)_____, an agreement to lay down arms without declaring victory or defeat.

9. A nationalist representative of Vietnam, _____, went to Versailles seeking self-determination for his country but was ignored.

10. In 1952, a military coup led by _____ overthrew the government in Egypt.

Choose the one alternative that best completes the statement or answers the question.

1. The event that triggered the outbreak of World War I was the
a. invasion of Poland by the Germans.
b. assassination of Archduke Ferdinand by a Serbian nationalist.
c. murder of the German emperor by a disgruntled soldier.
d. escape of Lenin to Russia.

2. Which of the following was *NOT* a feature of the war on the home front between 1914 and 1919?
a. Governments organized the major sectors of the economy for war production.
b. Executive branches of government increasingly took over from parliaments.
c. Governments controlled public opinion through the manipulation of mass media.
d. Despite shortages of manpower, governments kept women out of the work force.

3. Which of the following was *NOT* included in the final set of treaties that ended World War I?
a. A League of Nations was formed.
b. Russia was rewarded for its service to the Allies by the grant of substantial territories in Poland and the Baltic republics.
c. Germany was forced to accept blame for the war.
d. Austria-Hungary was divided up into a Germanic Austria as well as the independent states of Hungary and Czechoslovakia.

4. Which of the following statements concerning the British administration of India in the last decades of the 19th century is most accurate?
a. The British demilitarization of India caused substantial unemployment.
b. The enlightened British policy, begun in the 1880s, of fostering Indian industrialization began to improve the Indian economy.
c. British emphasis on the production of cash crops led to shortages of food production.
d. Indian economic dependency on Britain was beginning to end.

5. Who was the first Indian leader with a genuine mass following?
a. J. Nehru
b. M. Gandhi
c. M. A. Jinnah
d. B. G. Tilak

6. Which statement most accurately describes Mohandas Gandhi's appeal as a leader?
a. His image as a traditional mystic lost him the support of middle-class, educated Indians.
b. His blend of traditional images and a strong awareness of the world won him support among both middle-class and peasant Indians.
c. His ability to lead rested almost entirely on his legendary negotiating skills.
d. He was largely a charismatic figurehead, while the real work of leadership was handled by others.

7. What incident enabled the British occupation of Egypt in 1882?
a. the Dinshawai incident
b. the Mahdist revolt
c. the mutiny of Ahmad Orabi
d. the Suez Canal crisis

8. The Balfour Declaration
a. offered secret U.S. support to Britain and France in 1914.
b. recognized the Turkish republic.
c. was a German memorandum seeking Mexican support during World War I.
d. promised British support for a Jewish state in the Middle East.

9. After World War I, the Egyptian nationalist movement was centralized increasingly in what political party?
a. Liberal Constitutionalist
b. Union
c. Convention Peoples
d. Wafd

10. Which of the following best characterizes the political situation in the African colonies after World War I?
a. While the war fostered nationalism among intellectuals, society as a whole remained calm.
b. The political circumstances in Africa did not change as a result of the war.
c. The failure of the Europeans to keep promises made during the war fostered unrest.
d. Many African colonies saw the rise of non-violent protest movements that imitated Gandhi's program of satyagraha.

READING REVIEW: MAKING CONNECTIONS

The following questions are intended to emphasize important ideas within the chapter.

1. What were the causes leading to World War I?

2. How was the outcome of World War I determined?

3. How did World War I change life on the home front?

4. In what way did the Peace of Paris contribute to political and economic upheaval after the war?

5. What forces led to the European loss of colonial dominance?

6. What was the Indian prototype of decolonization movements?

7. How did the early Egyptian nationalist movement vary from that of India?

8. Why was Gandhi critical to the all-India nationalist movement?

9. Discuss the settlement of the issue of Palestine after World War I.

CHAPTER 29
The World between the Wars: Revolutions, Depression, and Authoritarian Response

Complete the following exercises in order *as you read* the chapter.

INTRODUCTION

Chapter introductions are a valuable guide to the material you are about to read, telling you what topics will be covered and how they fit together. If you keep the "big picture" provided by the introduction in mind as you read the chapter, you will find it much easier to organize your notes, identify important information, and avoid getting lost in the details. With this in mind, re-read the introduction to Chapter 29. As you read, make a list of the key topics you expect to learn about.

Key Topics

_____

_____

_____

_____

_____

_____

_____

_____

_____

_____

_____

_____

_____

_____

_____

_____

_____

_____

1. THE ROARING TWENTIES

As you read this section in y our textbook, complete the following outline to describe the key events and developments of the 1920s.

I. Bouncing Back?

      A. The West at Mid-Decade

2. REVOLUTION: THE FIRST WAVES

As you read this section of your textbook, complete the table below to compare and contrast the postwar revolutionary movements in Mexico, Russia, and China.

Revolutions in Mexico, Russia, and China		
Mexico	**Russia**	**China**
• By 1910 the regime of Porfirio Diaz was extremely vulnerable.		

3. THE GREAT GLOBAL DEPRESSION

As you read this section of your textbook, complete the chart below to trace the causes of the Great Depression, its social and economic consequences, and the responses of to the global economic crisis.

Causes of the Great Depression		
Causes	**Consequences**	**Responses**
• Overproduction of food led to falling crop prices.		

4. THE AUTHORITARIAN RESPONSE

As you read this section in your textbook, complete the following outline to describe the spread of authoritarian governments around the world during the 1930s.

I. The Rise of Nazism

    A. Postwar Germany

CHAPTER REVIEW

TERMS, EVENTS, PEOPLE

The following terms, people, and events are important to your understanding of the chapter. Define each one.

Kellogg-Briand Pact (1928)

Cubist movement

Fascism

Benito Mussolini
Syndicalism

British Commonwealth of Nations

Henry Ford

Mexican Revolution, 1910–1920

Francisco Madero

Pancho Villa

Emiliano Zapata

Victoriano Herta

Alvaro Obregón

Mexican Constitution of 1917

Lázaro Cárdenas

Diego Rivera and José Clemente Orozco

Corridos

Cristeros

Party of Institutionalized Revolution (PRI)

Soviet

Aleksander Kerensky

Russian Communist Party

Council of People's Commissars

Social Revolutionary Party

Congress of Soviets

Red Army

New Economic Policy (NEP)

Union of Soviet Socialist Republics (U.S.S.R.)

Supreme Soviet

Comintern

Joseph Stalin

Collectivization

Yuan Shikai

Sun Yatsen

May Fourth Movement

Li Dazhao

Guomindang (National Party)

Whampoa Military Academy

Chiang Kai-shek

Mao Zedong

Long March

Popular Front

New Deal

Totalitarian state

Popular Front

New Deal

Totalitarian state

Gestapo

Spanish Civil War .

Import substitution economies

Corporatism

Getúlio Vargas

Juan Perón

Eva Duarte (Evita)

Tojo Hideki

Spanish Civil War

Import substitution economies

MY KEY TERMS

Write down terms that are unfamiliar. How are the words used? Do other words or examples reveal their meaning? Try to figure out meaning from the context.

SHORT ANSWER REVIEW

Write the word or phrase that best completes each statement or answers the question.

1. In art, Pablo Picasso headed the _____ movement, which rendered familiar objects as geometric shapes.

2. After World War I, the United States in the West and _____ in Asia emerged as major economic competitors to Europe.

3. In 1922, the Italian king called on _____ to form a new government.

4. A central European nation created at Versailles out of Austria-Hungary and expanded from Serbia was _____.

5. More than Canada, the settler society _____ strongly emphasized social legislation.

6. Through their research and development programs, U.S. corporations invented artificial fibers like rayon and _____.

7. The Mexican revolutionary _____ used the motto "Land and Liberty" to express his political goals.

8. In the Mexican Revolution, _____, women who sometimes took up arms, participated in the rebellion against Díaz.

9. In Russia's revolution, a council of workers, or _____, took over the capital city government and arrested the tsar's ministers.

10. The greatest rival for power in China in the 1920s and 1930s was the _____ Party, or Guomindang.

Choose the one alternative that best completes the statement or answers the question.

1. Which of the following was *NOT* a feature of European society after World War I?
a. Women in Germany lost the right to vote they had gained during World War I.
b. The cubist movement, led by Pablo Picasso, developed in art.
c. Western Europe failed to regain the export markets it lost during the war.
d. New mass consumption items, like the radio, became important.

2. Which of the following reforms was *NOT* included in the Mexican Constitution of 1917?
a. the state takeover of property belonging to the Catholic Church
b. limits on foreign ownership of key resources
c. land reform
d. guaranteed rights for workers

3. How did Stalin's view of Communism differ from that of Lenin?
a. Lenin was only interested in the Russian Revolution and did not visualize any further revolutionary process.
b. Lenin was more interested in including a broad swath of the Russian population in the Communist movement.
c. Stalin concentrated on a strongly nationalist version of Communism and concentrated on socialism in one country.
d. Stalin was not a member of the Communist party.

4. Sun Yat-sen was the
a. first leader of the Communist discussion group at the University of Beijing.
b. most powerful regional warlord of northern China.
c. leader of the Revolutionary Alliance and first elected president of China.
d. head of the Whampoa Military Academy.

5. How did most Western governments respond to the Great Depression?
a. with concerted policies of cooperation to restart global trade
b. by encouraging industrialization in the colonies to expand trade
c. by taking a hands-off approach to the economy to give businesses freedom to act
d. with nationalist and protectionist policies that restricted global trade

6. Franklin Delano Roosevelt's New Deal emphasized what kind of polices?
a. unemployment benefits, Social Security, and public works program to create jobs
b. protectionism and a crackdown on labor unions
c. an elimination of government planning for the economy to give business more freedom
d. the deregulation of the banking industry

7. The National Socialist Party rose to power in what country prior to World War II?
a. Italy
b. Germany
c. Russia
d. Britain

8. What military leader in Argentina broadened the base of support for populist government by appealing to labor groups and the poor?
a. Juan Perón
b. Victoriano Huerta
c. Juan Arevalo
d. Getúlio Vargas

9. Why did Japan decide to pursue an aggressive policy of conquest in China?
a. Nationalist politicians convinced Japanese voters to elect an highly imperialistic government..
b. Japan felt compelled to respond to a powerful Chinese government that was massing troops for a potential invasion of Japan.
c. The Japanese military pursued this policy largely independent of more moderate civilian politicians and a more moderate electorate.
d. Japan's ally Germany demanded that Japan take a more aggressive stance.

10. The Soviet Politburo under Stalin
a. was composed of powerful commissars who were virtually independent of the central administration.
b. was particularly innovative in proposing new solutions to the endemic problems of Soviet society.
c. was a rubber stamp for Stalin and lived in fear of him.
d. was an open institution filled by the numerous new admissions to the Communist party.

READING REVIEW: MAKING CONNECTIONS

After reading and studying the chapter, review your understanding by answering each of the following questions, which emphasize important ideas within the chapter.

1. Characterize the *Roaring 20s*.

2. What factors led to the rise of the Fascists in Italy?

3. What changes occurred as a result of the Mexican Revolution?

4. What was the basis for Lenin and Stalin's domestic and economic policies, and how did they differ?

5. Why did the Nationalist party fail to achieve permanent success in China?

6. What were the causes of the Great Depression?

7. What was the worldwide impact of the Depression of the 1930s?

8. How did populist governments in Brazil and Argentina attempt to rule?

9. Discuss the Japanese government in the 1920s. How was the military able to gain influence?

CHAPTER 30
A Second Global Conflict and the End of the European World Order

Complete the following exercises in order *as you read* the chapter.

INTRODUCTION

Chapter introductions are a valuable guide to the material you are about to read, telling you what topics will be covered and how they fit together. If you keep the "big picture" provided by the introduction in mind as you read the chapter, you will find it much easier to organize your notes, identify important information, and avoid getting lost in the details. With this in mind, re-read the introduction to Chapter 30. As you read, make a list of the key topics you expect to learn about.

Key Topics

_____

_____

_____

_____

_____

_____

_____

_____

_____

_____

_____

_____

_____

_____

_____

_____

_____

_____

1. Old and New Causes of a Second World War

As you read this section of your textbook, complete the list below of the causes of the Second World War.

Causes of the Second World War

1. The gradual militarization of Japan

2. The rise of the Guomindang in China

3.

4.

5.

6.

7.

8.

---

2. UNCHECKED AGGRESSION AND THE COMING OF WAR IN EUROPE AND THE PACIFIC

As you read this section in your textbook, complete the table included below to compare and contrast global reaction to Japanese aggression in China and Germany aggression in Europe.

Global Responses to Aggression	
Japan	**Germany**
• Japan launched a massive invasion of China in 1937.	

3. THE CONDUCT OF A SECOND GLOBAL WAR

As you read this section in your textbook, complete the following outline to trace the course of World War II.

I. Nazi Blitzkrieg, Stalemate, and the Long Retreat

    A. Blitzkrieg

4. WAR'S END AND THE EMERGENCE OF THE SUPERPOWER STANDOFF

As you read this section of your textbook, complete the table below to compare and contrast the efforts made at Tehran, Yalta, and Potsdam to reduce tensions between the Soviet Union and its wartime allies and to shape the postwar world.

Debating the Postwar Settlement		
Tehran	**Yalta**	**Potsdam**
• Allies agree on an invasion of occupied France.		

5. Nationalism and Decolonization in South and Southeast Asia and Africa

As you read this section in your textbook, complete the following outline to describe the postwar process of decolonization in South and Southeast Asia and Africa.

I. The Winning of Independence in South and Southeast Asia

    A. India

CHAPTER REVIEW

TERMS, EVENTS, PEOPLE

The following terms, people, and events are important to your understanding of the chapter. Define each one.

National Soviet (Nazi) Party

Blitzkrieg

Vichy

Winston Churchill

Battle of Britain

Siege of Stalingrad

Holocaust

Battle of the Bulge

Pearl Harbor

Battles of the Coral Sea and Midway Island

Hiroshima and Nagasaki

United Nations

Teheran Conference (1944)

Yalta Conference (1945)

Potsdam Conference (1945)

Atlantic Charter

Quit India movement

Muslim League

Muhammad Ali Jinnah

Kwame Nkrumah

Land Freedom Army

Jomo Kenyatta

National Liberation Front (FLN)

Secrete Army Organization (OAS) .

Afrikaner National Party

MY KEY TERMS

Write down terms that are unfamiliar. How are the words used? Do other words or examples reveal their meaning? Try to figure out meaning from the context.

Write the word or phrase that best completes each statement or answers the question.

1. The Axis powers of Germany, Italy, and Japan signed an alliance called the
   _____.

2. The English prime minister who showed determination and a positive attitude to the public throughout the war was _____.

3. Japanese soldiers were especially brutal to the Chinese civilians living in the Guomindang capital, _____ .

4. U.S. president Roosevelt called for "the right of all people to choose the form of government under which they live" in the WWII agreement with Britain, the _____.

5. Nazi Germany's policy called the "_____" led to the death of about 6 million Jews in what came to be known as the Holocaust.

6. The Indian leader who supported a separate Muslim state called Pakistan was
   _____.

7. The turning point battle in the Pacific war, which saw the Japanese lose several aircraft carriers, was at _____.

8. The first atomic bomb was dropped on the Japanese city of _____ .

9. The last German offensive of the war was called the Battle of the _____.

10. South Africa imposed a rigid system of racial segregation called _____.

Choose the one alternative that best completes the statement or answers the question.

1. Which of the following regions was the first to be conquered by the Japanese?
a. Manchuria
b. Malaya
c. Singapore
d. Taiwan

2. Which of the following statements concerning World War II is *NOT* accurate?
a. By 1940, the German *Blitzkrieg* had swept over Poland, Denmark, Norway, Holland, Belgium, and France.
b. Japan's early military campaigns in China were carefully coordinated with German and Italian military maneuvers.
c. The United States entered World War II only in 1941 after the bombing of Pearl Harbor.
d. The German invasion of Poland forced Britain and France to declare war.

3. The genocidal campaign against the Jews by the Nazis was planned at:
a. the Tehran Conference.
b. the Yalta Conference.
c. the Wannsee Conference.
d. the Potsdam Conference.

4. The United Nations:
a. left China off the Security Council initially because of its civil war.
b. enabled the Western powers to maintain their monopoly on international relations.
c. was little changed from the League of Nations.
d. gave a greater voice to small countries than the League of Nations.

5. The Atlantic Charter of 1941:
a. enshrined the U.S. commitment to decolonization.
b. created an alliance between the United States and the Soviet Union.
c. committed the United States to restoring colonial rule to Southeast Asia.
d. formed the United Nations.

6. In India during World War II,
a. both the Muslim League and the Indian National strongly supported the British war effort.
b. the Muslim League and the Communists strongly supported the British war effort.
c. the Muslim League refused to support the British war without a promise of independence.
d. the British promised postwar independence, thus gaining widespread support for the war effort.

7. What radical African leader helped to achieve independence in Ghana?
a. Julius Nyerere
b. Jomo Kenyatta
c. Kwame Nkrumah
d. Nelson Mandela

8. Colonial societies with white settler populations
a. did not achieve independence in the 19th century.
b. were among the first to grant majority rule.
c. introduced the tactics of peaceful mass demonstrations and boycotts.
d. were the regions where overt violence and revolution were most likely to occur.

9. From 1948, South African politics were dominated by
a. the Afrikaner National Party.
b. the black leadership of the Zulu nation.
c. Nelson Mandela.
d. a U.N. mandate government dominated by the United States.

10. The original United Nations partition of Palestine in 1948
a. gave Jerusalem to the new Jewish state.
b. set borders that held until 1967.
c. gave Jerusalem to the new Arab state.
d. quickly resulted in war.

READING REVIEW: MAKING CONNECTIONS

After reading and studying the chapter, review your understanding by answering each of the following questions, which emphasize important ideas within the chapter.

1. What caused the outbreak of World War II?

2. How was the outcome of World War II determined?

3. How were the diplomatic problems of World War II settled?

4. What was the Cold War and how did it come about?

5. What were the two paths to independence in nonsettler Africa?

6. What was the tradition of decolonization in the settler colonies? How did South Africa's experience differ?

CHAPTER 31

Western Society and Eastern Europe in the Decades of the Cold War

Complete the following exercises in order *as you read* the chapter.

INTRODUCTION

Chapter introductions are a valuable guide to the material you are about to read, telling you what topics will be covered and how they fit together. If you keep the "big picture" provided by the introduction in mind as you read the chapter, you will find it much easier to organize your notes, identify important information, and avoid getting lost in the details. With this in mind, re-read the introduction to Chapter 31. As you read, make a list of the key topics you expect to learn about.

Key Topics

_____

_____

_____

_____

_____

_____

_____

_____

_____

_____

_____

_____

_____

_____

_____

_____

_____

1. AFTER WORLD WAR II: A NEW INTERNATIONAL SETTING FOR THE WEST

As you read this section in your textbook, fill in the chart below to summarize consequences of the Cold War in the Soviet Union, Europe, and the United States.

FOCUS QUESTION: *What were the military and political consequences of the Cold War in the Soviet Union, Europe, and the United States?*

Consequences of the Cold War		
United States	**Europe**	**Soviet Union**
• Formed military alliance called North Atlantic Treaty Organization (NATO)	• The Cold War divided Europe—communities ruled in the East and democracies were in the West.	• Created military alliance called the Warsaw Pact

Using the information in your chart, write a brief answer to the Focus Question.

2. THE RESURGENCE OF WESTERN EUROPE

As you read this section in your textbook, complete the table below to describe key developments in Western Europe in the postwar era.

Postwar Western Europe		
Government and Politics	**Foreign Affairs**	**Economic Expansion**
• Fascism and rightist movements were discredited.		

3. COLD WAR ALLIES: THE UNITED STATES, CANADA, AUSTRALIA, AND NEW ZEALAND

As you read this section in your textbook, create a timeline of key events in postwar American history.

The United States Since 1945

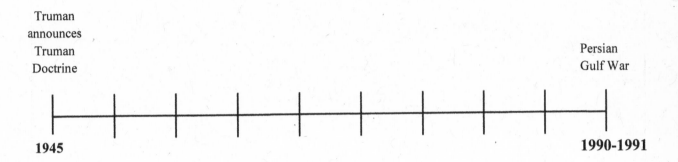

Truman
announces
Truman
Doctrine

Persian
Gulf War

1945

1990-1991

4. CULTURE AND SOCIETY IN THE WEST

As you read this section in your textbook, complete the following outline to describe important social and cultural trends in the postwar West.

I. Social Structure

       A. The Easing of Social Conflict

5. EASTERN EUROPE AFTER WORLD WAR II: A SOVIET EMPIRE

As you read this section in your textbook, complete the table below to describe key developments in Soviet-dominated Eastern Europe in the postwar era.

The Soviet Empire	
Soviet Control of Eastern Europe	**Soviet Domestic Policies**
• After World War II, the Soviets made it clear that they meant to stay in Eastern Europe.	

6. SOVIET CULTURE: PROMOTING BELIEFS AND INSTITUTIONS

As you read this section in your textbook, complete the concept web below to describe the main features of postwar Soviet culture.

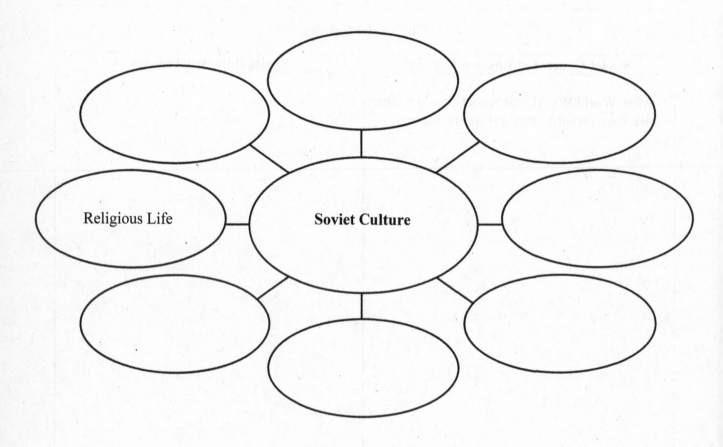

TERMS, EVENTS, PEOPLE

The following terms, people, and events are important to your understanding of the chapter. Define each one.

Cold war

Eastern bloc

Harry Truman

Iron curtain

Marshall Plan

North Atlantic Treaty Organization (NATO)

Warsaw Pact

Welfare state

Technocrat

Green movement

Margaret Thatcher and Ronald Reagan

European Union

New feminism

Simone de Beauvoir and Betty Friedan

Berlin Wall

Solidarity

Socialist realism

Alexsandr Solzhenitsyn

Nikita Khrushchev

Sputnik

MY KEY TERMS

Write down terms that are unfamiliar. How are the words used? Do other words or examples reveal their meaning? Try to figure out meaning from the context.

SHORT ANSWER REVIEW

Write the word or phrase that best completes each statement or answers the question.

1. The Soviet leader who came to power after Stalin's death was _____.

2. The author of *The Second Sex*, _____, began the feminist movement of the post-World War II era.

3. Author of *The Gulag Archipelago*, _____, was exiled to the United States.

4. The clearest extension of Soviet power immediately after World War II was in eastern _____.

5. The Swedish movie director _____ produced a series of dark psychological dramas.

6. Scientists Crick and Watson shared credit in the 1950s for discovering the basic genetic building block, _____.

7. Greater wealth in U.S. universities drew many academics from Europe, leading to what was called the _____ from Europe to the U.S.

8. The U.S. doctrine of containment was first applied in _____ and Turkey.

9. Separatists in the province of _____ in Canada failed to gain full independence.

10. The European nation that experienced the greatest economic growth was _____.

Choose the one alternative that best completes the statement or answers the question.

1. What American plan for economic aid to Europe after World War II helped initiate the Cold War?
a. the Schlieffen Plan
b. the Truman Doctrine
c. the Marshall Plan
d. NATO

2. Which of the following was a military alliance under U.S. leadership against the Soviet Union?
a. the E.E.C.
b. the Warsaw Pact
c. NATO
d. Unicef

3. Which of the following statements concerning the European welfare state is most accurate?
a. The imposition of the welfare state was accompanied by the elimination of the private sector in most European nations.
b. Middle-class people failed to realize any benefits from the welfare state.
c. The welfare state cushioned citizens against unusual hardship, but did not rearrange the overall social structure.
d. By redistributing income, the welfare state largely eliminated Western Europe's unequal class system.

4. After 1968, the majority of the French labor force was
a. working for the government.
b. working in factories.
c. part of the agriculture sector.
d. part of the service sector.

5. In the later 20th century, who emerged as Australia and New Zealand's main economic partners?
a. Japan and the United States
b. China
c. India and the Middle East
d. France and Britain

6. The new feminism that emerged after the 1949 publication of *The Second Sex* emphasized
a. a return to domestic life.
b. getting the vote for women.
c. the needs of women in the developing world.
d. a more literal equality that redefined what it meant to be male or female.

7. Which of the following nations remained independent of direct Soviet control after 1948?
a. Poland
b. Yugoslavia
c. Czechoslovakia
d. Hungary

8. Which of the following statements concerning the status of women in the Soviet Union is most accurate?
a. Women in the Soviet Union remained employed almost entirely in domestic services.
b. Soviet women were idealized according to the cult of domesticity popular in the West.
c. Soviet women dominated some professions, such as medicine, although they received less pay than men.
d. Soviet women continued to be denied the right to vote long after suffrage was granted in the West.

9. What leader emerged to take primary power in the Soviet Union in 1956?
a. Nikita Khrushchev
b. Mikhail Gorbachev
c. Yuri Andropov
d. Joseph Stalin

10. Which of the following was characteristic of workers in the Soviet Union during the 1980s?
a. declining alcoholism, which led to improved productivity
b. a tendency to erupt in violent strikes in the face of rising economic problems
c. a growing sense of sense of autonomy and opportunity, motivating them to be more productive
d. a lack of motivation for great diligence due to bureaucracy and the lack of consumer goods

READING REVIEW: MAKING CONNECTIONS

After reading and studying the chapter, review your understanding by answering each of the following questions, which emphasize important ideas within the chapter.

1. How did the Cold War affect Western Europe?

2. Characterize the internal politics of Western Europe after World War II.

3. What was the "welfare state"?

4. How did the social structure of the West change in the period after World War II?

5. Describe Western science and culture in the late 20th century.

6. How did Soviet foreign policy change after 1941?

7. What was the cultural policy of the Stalinist state?

CHAPTER 32
Latin America: Revolution and Reaction into the 21st Century

Complete the following exercises in order *as you read* the chapter.

INTRODUCTION

Chapter introductions are a valuable guide to the material you are about to read, telling you what topics will be covered and how they fit together. If you keep the "big picture" provided by the introduction in mind as you read the chapter, you will find it much easier to organize your notes, identify important information, and avoid getting lost in the details. With this in mind, re-read the introduction to Chapter 32. As you read, make a list of the key topics you expect to learn about.

Key Topics

_____

_____

_____

_____

_____

_____

_____

_____

_____

_____

_____

_____

_____

_____

_____

_____

_____

_____

_____

_____

_____

_____

1. LATIN AMERICA AFTER WORLD WAR II

As you read this section in your textbook, complete the table below to identify the competing forces for continuity and change in postwar Latin America.

Continuity and Change in Latin America	
Continuity	**Change**
• Persistence of authoritarian governments	

2. RADICAL OPTIONS IN THE 1950s

As you read this section in your textbook, complete the table below to compare and contrast the revolutionary movements in Guatemala and Cuba.

Latin American Revolutions	
Guatemala	**Cuba**
• Social and economic conditions in Guatemala were among the worst in the region.	

3. THE SEARCH FOR REFORM AND THE MILITARY OPTION

As you read this section in your textbook, complete the following outline to describe the struggle between authoritarian and democratic forces in recent Latin American political history.

I. Out of the Barracks: Soldiers Take Charge

    A. The Communist Threat

4. SOCIETIES IN SEARCH OF CHANGE

As you read this section of your textbook, complete the list below detailing major trends in recent Latin American social history.

Latin American Social History
1. Enfranchisement of Indian populations
2. Emergence of a Latin American women's movement
3.
4.
5.
6.
7.
8.

CHAPTER REVIEW

TERMS, EVENTS, PEOPLE

The following terms, people, and events are important to your understanding of the chapter. Define each one.

Third world

Party of Institutionalized Revolution (PRI)

Zapatistas

North American Free Trade Agreement (NAFTA)

Juan José Arevalo

United Fruit Company

Fulgencio Batista

Ernesto "Che" Guevara

Fidel Castro
Sandinista party

Liberation theology

Salvador Allende

Banana republics

Good Neighbor Policy

Alliance for Progress

Favelas

Jorge Luis Borges and Gabriel García Marquez

MY KEY TERMS

Write down terms that are unfamiliar. How are the words used? Do other words or examples reveal their meaning? Try to figure out meaning from the context.

SHORT ANSWER REVIEW

Write the word or phrase that best completes each statement or answers the question.

1. The developing nations are often referred to as the _____.

2. In the 1990s, the U.S., Canada, and Mexico formed an economic agreement called _____.

3. The U.S. governmental agency known as the _____ trained dissidents to invade Guatemala and later Cuba.

4. The authoritarian leader of Cuba before the Castro-led revolution was _____.

5. An economic, social, and political movement in Latin America that fused Catholic theology and socialism was known as _____.

6. The Marxist government in Nicaragua that was removed in an election in 1990 was led by the _____ party.

7. Corrupt governments led by strongmen and funded by export of tropical products were known as _____.

8. In 1948, the United Nations listed basic liberties to all people with the publication of the _____.

9. Inequalities based on _____ continued in some places in Latin America into the 21st century.

10. The Argentine dance made popular worldwide in the early 20th century was the _____.

Choose the one alternative that best completes the statement or answers the question.

1. What distinguishes Latin America from other Third World regions?
a. earlier independence and more Western social and political forms.
b. a general avoidance of military regimes.
c. a strong capacity to remain economically independent from developed nations.
d. a far greater tendency to adopt socialist political and economic models.

2. In 1994, the Zapatistas rose in rebellion in what country?
a. Chile
b. Mexico
c. Peru
d. Guatemala

3. Which of the following was *NOT* involved in the campaign to remove Jacobo Arbenz from power in Guatemala?
a. the Central Intelligence Agency
b. the United Fruit Co.
c. dissident Guatemalan military forces
d. the U.S. Marines

4. Which of the following statements most accurately describes the outcome of the Cuban revolution?
a. Extensive social reforms were accompanied by a failure to diversify the economy.
b. The Cuban government was able to maintain its independence from both the United States and the USSR.
c. The liberal government that resulted from the revolution returned to the constitution of 1940.
d. Economic reforms moved Cuba away from sugar production to a more industrialized economy.

5. Which of these best characterizes Christian Democratic parties in Latin America?
a. They supported traditionalist Catholic governments that prevented reforms.
b. They combined Catholic theology with socialist principles.
c. They hoped to bring reforms though popularly based mass parties that preempted the left.
d. They were closely linked to the military dictatorships that killed thousand in the 1970s and 1980s.

6. Which of the following was *NOT* typical of military governments in Latin America during the 1960s and 1970s?
a. repression of human rights
b. support for labor groups and the working class
c. bureaucratic organization similar to a military chain of command
d. stringent measures to control inflation

7. What U.S. president introduced the Good Neighbor Policy?
a. Theodore Roosevelt
b. Calvin Coolidge
c. Franklin Roosevelt
d. Harry Truman

8. Which of the following was *NOT* a problem for Latin American countries in the late 20th century?
a. tremendous levels of debt that threatened economic stability
b. the international drug trade
c. high rates of inflation
d. the return of military rule

9. In which of the following periods did most Latin American women achieve the right to vote?
a. just prior to World War I
b. in the 1920s and 1930s
c. in the 1940s and 1950s
d. in the 1960s and 1970s

10. The Latin American authors who wrote in a style known as "magical realism"
a. were reviving a technique first developed in 18th century Mexico.
b. found the reality of Latin America too absurd to be described with traditional forms.
c. were, like many earlier Latin American authors, imitating French literary styles.
d. avoided Latin American themes, in favor of mythical stories of gods and goddesses.

READING REVIEW: MAKING CONNECTIONS

After reading and studying the chapter, review your understanding by answering each of the following questions, which emphasize important ideas within the chapter.

1. What problems were associated with Latin America's attempt to achieve economic development?

2. How was radical reform attempted in Guatemala? What was the result?

3. Why did the military believe that they offered a viable answer to Latin American problems? What was the outcome of military governments?

4. How has the role of women changed in Latin America in the twentieth century?

5. What has been the pattern of U.S. interaction with Latin America?

6. How have population movements affected the development of Latin America in the twentieth century?

CHAPTER **33**
Africa, the Middle East, and Asia in the Era of Independence

Complete the following exercises in order *as you read* the chapter.

INTRODUCTION

Chapter introductions are a valuable guide to the material you are about to read, telling you what topics will be covered and how they fit together. If you keep the "big picture" provided by the introduction in mind as you read the chapter, you will find it much easier to organize your notes, identify important information, and avoid getting lost in the details. With this in mind, re-read the introduction to Chapter 33. As you read, make a list of the key topics you expect to learn about.

Key Topics

_____

_____

_____

_____

_____

_____

_____

_____

_____

_____

_____

_____

_____

_____

_____

_____

_____

_____

_____

1. THE CHALLENGES OF INDEPENDENCE

As you read this section of your textbook, complete the concept web below to explore the challenges faced by newly independent countries in the postwar era.

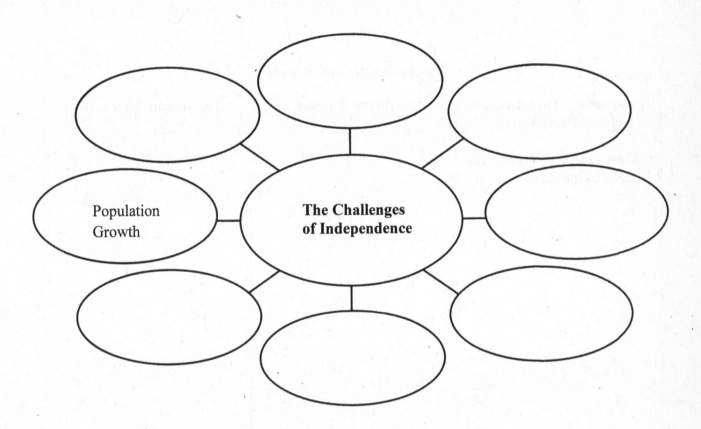

2. POST-COLONIAL OPTIONS FOR ACHIEVING ECONOMIC GROWTH AND SOCIAL JUSTICE

As you read this section of your textbook, complete the table below to compare and contrast three important post-colonial political options.

Post-Colonial Governments		
Charismatic Populists and One-Party Rule	**Military Options**	**The Indian Alternative**
• Many independence leaders retreated into authoritarian rule.		

3. DELAYED REVOLUTIONS: RELIGIOUS REVIVALISM AND LIBERATION MOVEMENTS IN SETTLER SOCIETIES

As you read this section in your textbook, complete the table below to compare and contrast revolutionary movements in Iran and South Africa.

	Iran	South Africa
Key Features of the Pre-Revolutionary Regime	Authoritarian rule backed up by American power	
Forces for Change	• Antipathy of the emerging Iranian middle class • Neglect of the military rank-and-file	

CHAPTER REVIEW

TERMS, EVENTS, PEOPLE

The following terms, people, and events are important to your understanding of the chapter. Define each one.

Bangladesh

Indira Gandhi

Corazon Aquino

Benazir Bhutto

Primary products

Neocolonialism

Kwame Nkrumah

Muslim Brotherhood

Hasan al-Banna

Gamal Abdul Nasser

Anwar Sadat

Hosni Mubarak

Jawaharlal Nehru

Green Revolution

Ayatollah Khomeini

Apartheid

Homelands

African National Congress (ANC)

Walter Sisulu and Steve Biko

Nelson Mandela

F.W. de Klerk.

MY KEY TERMS

Write down terms that are unfamiliar. How are the words used? Do other words or examples reveal their meaning? Try to figure out meaning from the context.

Write the word or phrase that best completes each statement or answers the question.

1. Backed by the Indians, the East Pakistanis won a war of secession that led to the establishment of the independent nation of _____ in 1972.

2. Iraq's _____ justified his 1990 annexation of Kuwait with the argument that the oil-rich nation was an artificial creation of the British colonizers, who had seized land that originally belonged to Iraq.

3. Most third world countries depend on the export of two or three food or industrial crops such as cocoa, palm oil, coffee, jute, or minerals. Such export commodities are called _____ products.

4. No military leader was more radical with regard to social and economic reform than Egypt's _____, who came to power in 1952.

5. Nasser's greatest foreign policy coup came in 1956, when he rallied international opinion to oust the British from the _____ zone.

6. The _____ Dam project, which was the cornerstone of Nasser's development drive, was something of a disaster.

7. Nasser's successor, _____, had little choice but to dismantle the massive state apparatus that had been created.

8. In many respects, the Iranian Revolution of 1979 under _____ represents a throwback to the religious fervor of anticolonial movements such as the Mahdist revolt in Sudan.

9. Racial separation was organized on a grander scale in South Africa by the creation of numerous _____, each designated for the main ethno-linguistic groups within the black African population.

10. Black organizations like the _____ were declared illegal, and African leaders were shipped off to maximum-security prisons.

MULTIPLE CHOICE REVIEW

Choose the one alternative that best completes the statement or answers the question.

1. Which of the following statements concerning the impact of colonizers on new nations is most accurate?
a. Europeans established the boundaries of their colonies on the basis of the traditional states and civilizations that had existed prior to Western imperialism.
b. Europeans carefully surveyed the boundary lines of their colonies to reduce disputes.
c. European colonization resulted in ethnic and religious homogeneity in the new nations.
d. Europeans hastily colonized Africa and established boundaries without reference to ethnic groups of cultural homogeneity.

2. Which of the following statements is *NOT* true?
a. Factors making for population growth only began to take effect in the late 19th century.
b. Colonial rule brought an end to local war that caused population losses.
c. New railroad links created by the colonizers cut down on regional famines.
d. Improved hygiene and medical treatment played little part in the population increase until the twentieth century.

3. One of the chief by-products of population growth in the Third World has been
a. industrialization.
b. mass migration to cities.
c. the imposition of effective birth control programs.
d. intensive programs of land redistribution.

4. Which statement best characterizes the status of women in newly independent states after World War II?
a. The role played by women in nationalist movements earned them important social gains.
b. Women played little role in nationalist movements, and saw no changes as a result.
c. Women in these countries often faced basic issues of survival, such as proper nutrition.
d. The influence of women like Indira Gandhi and Benazir Bhutto brought social equality to poor women in many countries.

5. Which of the following was *NOT* a common problem for developing nations after World War II?
a. overdependence on the export of primary products .
b. a neocolonial economy dominated by the industrialized nations.
c. widespread corruption in the educated ruling classes.
d. a lack of access to markets in the industrialized world.

6. The military in Third World nations
a. lacked the technical training found among the nationalist leaders.
b. were committed to the preservation of civilian rule.
c. were more resistant than other social groups to religious and ethnic divisions.
d. had little impact on the political structure of Third World nations.

7. After becoming the leader of Egypt, Gamal Abdul Nasser
a. placed stiff restrictions on foreign investment to foster Egypt's economic independence.
b. supported the policies of the Muslim Brotherhood.
c. was unable to take control of the Suez Canal from the British and the French.
d. sought a peaceful relationship with Israel.

8. In which of the following ways was India similar to Egypt following decolonization?
a. level of industrialization
b. emphasis on socialism and state intervention in the economy
c. military takeover of the government
d. size of the middle class

9. In Iran, the impetus for modernization resulted from
a. several decades of British rule.
b. the CIA's successful overthrow of a fundamentalist Islamic regime in 1953.
c. a indigenous middle-class reformist movement.
d. a sudden policy of modernization imposed from above by the Pahlavi shahs.

10. The end of apartheid in South Africa was brought about in part by
a. a violent large scale civil war instigated by the African National Congress.
b. the military occupation of South Africa by forces under the control of the United Nations.
c. international sanctions and failed initiatives in the wars in Namibia and Angola.
d. the failure of the USSR to supply critical arms shipments to the Nationalist government.

READING REVIEW: MAKING CONNECTIONS

After reading and studying the chapter, review your understanding by answering each of the following questions, which emphasize important ideas within the chapter.

1. Why was there such difficulty in the Third World establishing national identities?

2. What accounts for high population growth in the Third World?

3. How are Third World cities different from those of the West?

4. Define the term "neocolonialism."

5. In what way did Nasser's military government differ from other military regimes?

6. How did India differ from Egypt? How were the two governments the same?

7. In what ways did the Khomeini revolution of 1979 in Iran resemble the 19th-century Mahdist movement?

CHAPTER 34
Rebirth and Revolution: Nation-Building in East Asia and the Pacific Rim

Complete the following exercises in order *as you read* the chapter.

INTRODUCTION

Chapter introductions are a valuable guide to the material you are about to read, telling you what topics will be covered and how they fit together. If you keep the "big picture" provided by the introduction in mind as you read the chapter, you will find it much easier to organize your notes, identify important information, and avoid getting lost in the details. With this in mind, re-read the introduction to Chapter 34. As you read, make a list of the key topics you expect to learn about.

Key Topics

_____

_____

_____

_____

_____

_____

_____

_____

_____

_____

_____

_____

_____

_____

_____

_____

_____

1. EAST ASIA IN THE POSTWAR SETTLEMENTS

As you read this section of your textbook, complete the chart below to trace the Japan's postwar rise from defeated and devastated nation to global economic powerhouse.

Postwar Conditions	Politics and Culture	Economic Surge
• In 1945, Japan's economy lay in ruins.		

2. THE PACIFIC RIM: MORE JAPANS?

As you read this section of your textbook, complete the list below of the common factors that contributed to the economic growth of Pacific Rim states.

Economic Growth of Pacific Rim States

1. Governments played a key role in economic planning

2. Huge industrial groups controlled important industries

3.

4.

5.

6.

7.

8.

---

3. MAO'S CHINA: VANGUARD OF WORLD REVOLUTION?

As you read this section in your textbook, complete the following outline to trace the history of China under Mao's leadership.

I. The Japanese Invasion

    A. Nationalists and Communists

4. COLONIALISM AND REVOLUTION IN VIETNAM

As you read this section in your textbook, create a timeline of Vietnamese history from the late eighteenth century to 1975.

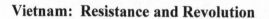

Vietnam: Resistance and Revolution

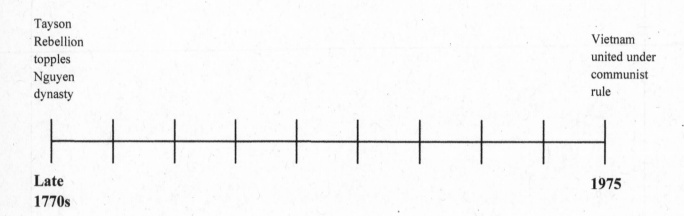

Tayson
Rebellion
topples
Nguyen
dynasty

Vietnam
united under
communist
rule

**Late
1770s**

1975

TERMS, EVENTS, PEOPLE

The following terms, people, and events are important to your understanding of the chapter. Define each one.

Singapore

Douglas MacArthur

Liberal Democratic Party

Republic of Korea

Democratic People's Republic of Korea

Korean War

Taiwan

Hong Kong

Hyundai

Lee Kuan Yew

Mass Line

Great Leap Forward

Zhou Enlai, Deng Xiaoping, and Liu Shaoqui

Jiang Qing

People's Liberation Army

Cultural Revolution

Lin Bao

People's Republic of China

Red Guard

Gang of Four

Tayson Rebellion

Nguyen Anh (Gia Long)

Minh Mang

Vietnamese Nationalist Party (VNQDD)

Communist Party of Vietnam

Ho Chi Minh (Nguyen Ai Quoc)

Viet Minh

Vo Nguyen Giap

Ngo Dinh Diem

Viet Cong

MY KEY TERMS

Write down terms that are unfamiliar. How are the words used? Do other words or examples reveal their meaning? Try to figure out meaning from the context.

SHORT ANSWER REVIEW

Write the word or phrase that best completes each statement or answers the question.

1. _____ retained a large British naval base until 1971, when Britain abandoned all pretense of power in east Asia.

2. The American occupation government, headed by General _____, worked quickly to tear down Japan's wartime political structure.

3. A 1955 merger of two moderate parties led to the new _____ Party that would monopolize Japan's government into the 1990s.

4. In 1948 the United States sponsored the_____ in the South of the Korean peninsula.

5. The northern half of the Korean peninsula was governed by the Soviet-dominated _____ of Korea.

6. North Korea quickly became a Communist state with Stalinist-type emphasis on the power of the leader, _____.

7. During the 1950s the South Korean regime was headed by the nationalist _____.

8. President Truman orchestrated the United Nations' sponsorship of a largely American "_____" in support of South Korean troops.

9. In the 1980s, Britain reached an agreement with China to turn over _____ to the Chinese in 1999.

10. _____ virtually governed Korea's southeastern coast through shipbuilding and company-supported housing and education networks.

MULTIPLE CHOICE REVIEW

Choose the one alternative that best completes the statement or answers the question.

1. Which of the following statements concerning the Japanese political system after World War II is most accurate?
a. The emperor remained the most powerful figure in the Japanese political system.
b. A single moderate party, the Liberal Democrats, emerged after 1955 to monopolize the Japanese political system.
c. Although the military suffered a setback as a result of the Japanese defeat, the general staff of the Japanese armies continued to influence virtually all political decisions.
d. Japanese politics was characterized by a huge number of parties, none of which could achieve a majority in the new parliament.

2. Which of the following statements most accurately reflects the situation in Korea following the Korean War?
a. Northern and southern Korea were rapidly reunited under a single government.
b. Northern Korea threw off its ties with China and the Soviet Union.
c. Korea remained divided with authoritarian governments in both halves of the nation.
d. Southern Korea became fully democratic but moved closer to political neutrality during the Cold War.

3. Japan produced a distinctive economic culture after the 1950s that included all of the following features *EXCEPT*
a. a strong tradition of independent unions.
b. managers who displayed active interest in suggestions by employees.
c. a network of policies and attitudes that reflected older traditions of group solidarity.
d. willingness among management to abide by collective decisions.

4. In the 1970s, which Asian nation surpassed Japan in steel production?
a. Malaysia.
b. Vietnam.
c. China.
d. South Korea.

5. Which of the following best characterizes the political status of Taiwan after 1978?
a. Taiwan remained autonomous from Beijing, although not officially recognized as independent by China or the United States.
b. Taiwan returned to rule by Communist China in 1978, with the same status as any other province.
c. Taiwan became a self-governing province within Communist China in 1978.
d. Taiwan remained a British protectorate, although with a high degree of self-rule.

6. Which of the following statements concerning the states of the Pacific Rim is most accurate?
a. Individualism was the hallmark of the economic development of this region.
b. The Pacific Rim states abandoned Confucian concepts in pursuit of Western culture.
c. Most of the states of the Pacific Rim limited dissent and depended on centralized government planning.
d. All of the states of the Pacific Rim benefited from having been former British colonies.

7. The Great Leap Forward
a. imposed a series of five-year plans intended to create an industrial technocracy.
b. brought China into closer relationship with the West.
c. pushed industrialization through small-scale projects in peasant communes.
d. resulted in the creation of small private plots for peasants.

8. After the death of Mao Zedong, China
a. returned to a policy of rigid central planning and state ownership of all property.
b. combined economic liberalization with more widespread democratic reforms
c. pursued capitalist development without democratic reforms.
d. stagnated economically, though it has pursued democratic reforms.

9. The Vietnamese dynasty that succeeded in uniting all of Vietnam under a single government in 1802 was the
a. Nguyen.
b. Trinh.
c. Tayson.
d. Qing.

10. In the aftermath of the Second Indochina War, Vietnam
a. pursued a hard-line Marxist-Leninist political and economic program.
b. enjoyed close relations with China, enabling it to develop its economy rapidly.
c. quickly reconciled with the United States, enabling it to receive significant relief funds.
d. suffered periodic civil war, which continues to stunt its economic growth.

After reading and studying the chapter, review your understanding by answering each of the following questions, which emphasize important ideas within the chapter.

1. What accounts for the enormous economic growth of Japan after 1955?

2. What was the political structure of Japan after 1955?

3. What themes were common among the states of the Pacific Rim?

4. What accounts for the common theme of growth in the Pacific Rim?

5. How did Mao's political beliefs affect the nature of Communist reforms until 1975?

6. How did France gain control of Vietnam?

7. How did the Japanese invasion of Indochina aid in the Communist success in Vietnam?

Power, Politics, and Conflict in World History, 1990–2010

Complete the following exercises in order *as you read* the chapter.

INTRODUCTION

Chapter introductions are a valuable guide to the material you are about to read, telling you what topics will be covered and how they fit together. If you keep the "big picture" provided by the introduction in mind as you read the chapter, you will find it much easier to organize your notes, identify important information, and avoid getting lost in the details. With this in mind, re-read the introduction to Chapter 35. As you read, make a list of the key topics you expect to learn about.

Key Topics

_____

_____

_____

_____

_____

_____

_____

_____

_____

_____

_____

_____

_____

_____

_____

_____

_____

_____

1. THE END OF THE COLD WAR

As you read this section in your textbook, complete the following outline to trace the decline and disintegration of the Soviet Union in the late twentieth century.

I. Factors in Soviet Decline

      A. A Failure of Leadership

2. THE SPREAD OF DEMOCRACY

As you read this section in your textbook, complete the table below to make a list of countries that moved towards democracy in the late twentieth century, as well as the common patterns and challenges experienced by newly democratic nations.

New Democracies	Common Patterns and Challenges
1. Spain	1. Link between democracy and economic growth
2. Portugal	2.
3.	3.
4.	4.
5.	5.
6.	6.
7.	7.
8.	8.

3. THE GREAT POWERS AND NEW DISPUTES

As you read this section in your textbook, complete the table included below to make a list of late twentieth-century conflicts, as well as the role of the Great Powers in precipitating or resolving them.

Conflicts	Involvement of the Great Powers
1. Chechnya uprising	1. Russia sent troops to suppress rebels
2.	2.
3.	3.
4.	4.
5.	5.
6.	6.
7.	7.
8.	8.

4. THE UNITED STATES AS SOLE SUPERPOWER

As you read this section of your textbook, complete the table below to describe the role of the United States in global political and economic affairs at the end of the twentieth century.

The United States and the World	
Politics	**Economics**
• Americans debated the role of the United States in resolving regional conflicts.	

TERMS, EVENTS, PEOPLE

The following terms, people, and events are important to your understanding of the chapter. Define each one.

Mikhail Gorbachev

Glasnost

Perestroika

Boris Yeltsin

Persian Gulf War

MY KEY TERMS

Write down terms that are unfamiliar. How are the words used? Do other words or examples reveal their meaning? Try to figure out meaning from the context.

Write the word or phrase that best completes each statement or answers the question.

1. If scientific predictions are correct, _____ will increasingly cause major shifts in temperatures and rainfall.

2. Many forecasts see the population of the world stabilizing by the year _____.

3. The organization originally created to block Soviet expansionism is called _____.

4. Tensions between India and Pakistan have centered on the disputed territory of _____.

5. Many experts see _____ as the dominant theme of present and future world history.

Choose the one alternative that best completes the statement or answers the question.

1. Which of the following statements concerning the Japanese political system after World War II is most accurate?
a. The emperor remained the most powerful figure in the Japanese political system.
b. A single moderate party, the Liberal Democrats, emerged after 1955 to monopolize the Japanese political system.
c. Although the military suffered a setback as a result of the Japanese defeat, the general staff of the Japanese armies continued to influence virtually all political decisions.
d. Japanese politics was characterized by a huge number of parties, none of which could achieve a majority in the new parliament.

2. Which of the following statements most accurately reflects the situation in Korea following the Korean War?
a. Northern and southern Korea were rapidly reunited under a single government.
b. Northern Korea threw off its ties with China and the Soviet Union.
c. Korea remained divided with authoritarian governments in both halves of the nation.
d. Southern Korea became fully democratic but moved closer to political neutrality during the Cold War.

3. Japan produced a distinctive economic culture after the 1950s that included all of the following features EXCEPT
a. a strong tradition of independent unions.
b. managers who displayed active interest in suggestions by employees.
c. a network of policies and attitudes that reflected older traditions of group solidarity.
d. willingness among management to abide by collective decisions.

4. In the 1970s, which Asian nation surpassed Japan in steel production?
a. Malaysia.
b. Vietnam.
c. China.
d. South Korea.

5. Which of the following best characterizes the political status of Taiwan after 1978?
a. Taiwan remained autonomous from Beijing, although not officially recognized as independent by China or the United States.
b. Taiwan returned to rule by Communist China in 1978, with the same status as any other province.
c. Taiwan became a self-governing province within Communist China in 1978.
d. Taiwan remained a British protectorate, although with a high degree of self-rule.

6. Which of the following statements concerning the states of the Pacific Rim is most accurate?
a. Individualism was the hallmark of the economic development of this region.
b. The Pacific Rim states abandoned Confucian concepts in pursuit of Western culture.
c. Most of the states of the Pacific Rim limited dissent and depended on centralized government planning.
d. All of the states of the Pacific Rim benefited from having been former British colonies.

7. The Great Leap Forward
a. imposed a series of five-year plans intended to create an industrial technocracy.
b. brought China into closer relationship with the West.
c. pushed industrialization through small-scale projects in peasant communes.
d. resulted in the creation of small private plots for peasants.

8. After the death of Mao Zedong, China
a. returned to a policy of rigid central planning and state ownership of all property.
b. combined economic liberalization with more widespread democratic reforms
c. pursued capitalist development without democratic reforms.
d. stagnated economically, though it has pursued democratic reforms.

9. The Vietnamese dynasty that succeeded in uniting all of Vietnam under a single government in 1802 was the
a. Nguyen.
b. Trinh.
c. Tayson.
d. Qing.

10. In the aftermath of the Second Indochina War, Vietnam
a. pursued a hard-line Marxist-Leninist political and economic program.
b. enjoyed close relations with China, enabling it to develop its economy rapidly.
c. quickly reconciled with the United States, enabling it to receive significant relief funds.
d. suffered periodic civil war, which continues to stunt its economic growth.

READING REVIEW: MAKING CONNECTIONS

After reading and studying the chapter, review your understanding by answering each of the following questions, which emphasize important ideas within the chapter.

1. What developments led to the breakup of the Soviet Union in 1991? How did the decline of the Soviet Union affect political developments in East Europe?

2. What forces drove the trend of democratization from the later 1970s onwards?

3. What have been the common elements of regional conflicts since the fall of the Soviet Union?

4. How have Western Europe and the United States responded to violent ethnic and regional conflict?

5. How have ethnic conflicts in Western Europe and Africa differed?

6. How has the United States role as sole superpower affected world politics?

7. What factors spurred anti-American terrorism since the fall of the Soviet Union?

CHAPTER 36
Globalization and Resistance

Complete the following exercises in order *as you read* the chapter.

INTRODUCTION

Chapter introductions are a valuable guide to the material you are about to read, telling you what topics will be covered and how they fit together. If you keep the "big picture" provided by the introduction in mind as you read the chapter, you will find it much easier to organize your notes, identify important information, and avoid getting lost in the details. With this in mind, re-read the introduction to Chapter 36. As you read, make a list of the key topics you expect to learn about.

Key Topics

_____

_____

_____

_____

_____

_____

_____

_____

_____

_____

_____

_____

_____

_____

_____

_____

1. GLOBALIZATION: CAUSES AND PROCESSES

As you read this section in your textbook, complete the following concept web to describe the multifaceted phenomenon of globalization.

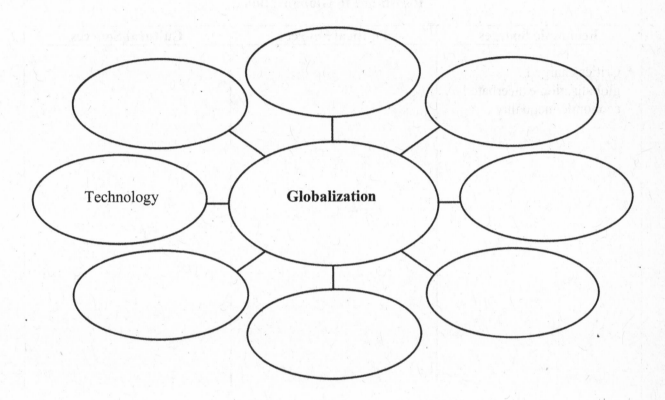

2. RESISTANCE AND ALTERNATIVES

As you read this section of your textbook, complete the table below to describe the political, economic, and cultural sources of resistance to globalization.

Resistance to Globalization		
Economic Sources	**Political Sources**	**Cultural Sources**
• Critics charged globalization exacerbated economic inequality.		

3. THE GLOBAL ENVIRONMENT

As you read this section of your textbook, complete the list below of the environmental consequences of globalization in general and global industrial development in particular.

Environmental Consequences

1. Economic growth brought with it new environmental pressures

2. Newly industrialized nations added to global pollution

3.

4.

5.

6.

7.

8.

4. TOWARD THE FUTURE

As you read this section in your textbook, complete the table included below to identify trends that may continue in coming decades, as well as big changes that may be in store for the world.

Trends	Changes
1. Global population growth will continue to slow	1. Climate change may have dramatic consequences
2.	2.
3.	3.
4.	4.
5.	5.
6.	6.

TERMS, PEOPLE, EVENTS

The following terms, people, and events are important to your understanding of the chapter. Write a brief definition of each.

Globalization

Multinational corporations

North American Free Trade Agreement (NAFTA)

MY KEY TERMS

Write down terms that are unfamiliar. How are the words used? Do other words or examples reveal their meaning? Try to figure out meaning from the context.

SHORT ANSWER REVIEW

Write the word or phrase that best completes each statement or answers the question.

1. If scientific predictions are correct, _____ will increasingly cause major shifts in temperatures and rainfall.

2. Many forecasts see the population of the world stabilizing by the year _____.

3. The organization originally created to block Soviet expansionism is called _____.

4. Tensions between India and Pakistan have centered on the disputed territory of _____.

5. Many experts see _____ as the dominant theme of present and future world history.

6. By the close of the 1990s, the path to worldwide _____ has been caused by the adoption of Western cultural values, art forms, consumer goods, and the English language.

7. During the late 20th century the United Nations dealt with gender and population control issues, and combated the _____ epidemic.

8. In 2000 the wealthiest _____ of humanity dominated consumption and produced the most pollution.

MULTIPLE CHOICE REVIEW

Choose the one alternative that best completes the statement or answers the question.

1. Which of the following did *NOT* contribute to the collapse of the Soviet Union?
a. increased pressure from the United States
b. the spread of AIDS
c. environmental deterioration
d. industrial stagnation

2. The Soviet leader who instituted wide-reaching reforms in the 1980s was:
a. Mikhail Gorbachev.
b. Boris Yeltsin.
c. Slobodan Milosevic.
d. Vladimir Putin.

3. Glasnost and perestroika are Russian terms meaning:
a. openness and central planning.
b. central planning and economic restructuring.
c. openness and economic restructuring.
d. central planning and industrialization.

4. What was the immediate impact of market reforms in Poland in 1991?
a. rising prices and growing disaffection with the Solidarity government.
b. rapid industrialization and increased immigration from other countries.
c. a collapse of the Solidarity government and the return of the Communists.
d. slow but steady growth and nearly full employment.

5. Which of these best characterizes the Russian economy by the late 1990s?
a. full market reforms and strong economic performance
b. full market reforms accompanied by widespread corruption
c. strong economic performance accompanied by widespread corruption
d. poor economic performance and widespread corruption

6. Which region remained largely authoritarian in the 1990s?
a. Africa
b. Latin America
c. Eastern Europe
d. newly industrialized nations of the Pacific Rim

7. In which of the following places was ethnic conflict settled peacefully?
a. Chechnya
b. Czechoslovakia
c. Yugoslavia
d. Rwanda

8. As a result of the Persian Gulf War in 1991,
a. Kuwait became province of Iraq.
b. the United States established a large military presence in the region.
c. the Saudi Arabian government instituted strong democratic reforms.
d. relations between Palestinians and Israelis improved for a number of years.

9. In which country did violence between Hutus and Tutsis result in hundreds of thousands of deaths?
a. Sierra Leone.
b. Liberia.
c. Rwanda.
d. Sudan.

10. Which of the following has *NOT* been a factor in the rise of militant Islamic anti-American terrorism?
a. the U.S. alliance with Israel.
b. the stationing of U.S. troops in Saudi Arabia
c. U.S. support for authoritarian regimes in the Middle East.
d. U.S. military strikes against Islamic holy sites.

READING REVIEW: MAKING CONNECTIONS

After reading and studying the chapter, review your understanding by answering each of the following questions, which emphasize important ideas within the chapter.

1. What has enabled the increases in globalization?

2. What has been the impact of multinational corporations?

3. What role has migration played in globalization?

4. How has culture changed as a result of globalization?

5. How effective have government and international organizations been in controlling globalization?

6. How has globalization and increased industrialization effected the environment?